WEEPING WILLOW,

Why Are You Weeping?

To: A. Sivh

Very Special
Person + Keeping
making this world a
better place.

"Thank you"

Sena Hilton

WEEPING WILLOW,

Why Are You Weeping?

by Terra Wilson

First Edition 2020

Cover Art designed by Adriana Quintero
Edited by Porsché Mysticque Steele

ISBN 978-1-7357487-0-2 (paperback)
ISBN 978-1-7357487-1-9 (e-book)

DEDICATION

Wade F. and Symone L. U.R. love, joy, and happiness.
Walter and Marine, my parents. Thank you.
A host of family and friends. Mitch E., Rick, Mel, Nae, Debra E.,
Angela B., Janice T., David L., Karen W., Freddy G.,
D.W., Rita P., and my husband who said, "I did the best I could."

ACKNOWLEDGMENTS

*An incredibly special homage to Mrs. Rose from Philadelphia,
my fifth and sixth-grade teacher, and to the S.F.S.U.
education department. Their kindness and generosity showed me
that there is goodness in the world. I am a grateful student.*

TABLE OF CONTENTS

Introduction   1

- **Story One**   **4**

The Beginning   5

- **Story Two**   **8**

It's Only Whipped Cream   9

- **Story Three**   **18**

Highway 4 Angel   19

    Story Three Poetry   28

"The Gift"   29

- **Story Four**   **30**

What Is The Meaning Of Life?   31

    Story Four Poetry   44

"I Give"   45

"A Man In The House"   47

"Peace Baby Peace"   48

"My Home"   49

- **Story Five**   **50**

The Proposal   51

    Story Five Poetry   56

"Take My Hand"   57

"Absolutely"   58

"Just Right"   59

- **Story Six**   **61**

Baby, Sweet Baby   62

Story Six Poetry   68

"You"   69

- **Story Seven**   **71**

Little Sister   72

- **Story Eight**   **79**

Don't Get In That Car!   80

Story Eight Poetry   92

"The Purpose"   93

"Baby Let's Ride"   94

- **Story Nine**   **96**

The Motorcyclist   97

- **Story Ten**   **101**

The Airplane   102

- **Story Eleven**   **106**

Can I   107

- **Story Twelve**   **118**

The Computer   119

- **Story Thirteen**   **126**

The Van   127

Story Thirteen Poetry   141

"My Purpose Was You"   142

"Goodbyes"   143

"Celebrate You"   144

- **Story Fourteen**   **145**

Change Our World   146

Story Fourteen Poetry   153

"Don't Bully"   154

"A Place To Call Home"   156

- **Story Fifteen**   **158**

America, America   159

Story Fifteen Poetry   165

"Make A Difference"   166

- **Story Sixteen**   **168**

Hopes And Dreams At The Casino   169

Story Sixteen Poetry   180

"Rainbow"   181

- **Story Seventeen**   **182**

Bell   183

- **Story Eighteen**   **190**

Sweet Days Of Summer   191

- **Story Nineteen**   **197**

The Reveal   198

Story Nineteen Poetry   202

"I Thought"   203

"Blackness Is My Cover"   205

- **Story Twenty**   **207**

Little Marine   208

INTRODUCTION

Weeping willow trees are often used as symbolism for us to let go and turn a new corner in our lives and surrender to our innermost heart. We all know right from wrong and have the right of choice. All of us can survive, thrive, and adapt to any given situation. Like us, the weeping willow tree adapts well in any place the tree calls home. Weeping willow trees are also known as the trees of enchantment. I am sure on many occasions you have stared at the weeping trees and wondered. Right? The tree is sometimes silent without movement, but it's always watching. Perchance you are standing next to one when the wind blows the tree will whisper to you. Just listen. Weeping willow trees also symbolize freedom, healing, and love lost. It can encourage moving on with what is thrown at you in your life and even facing and moving from, some of the most challenging situations in everyday life.

I experienced my own life-changing encounter with an enchanting weeping willow tree. Nothing was known to me about the weeping willow tree until I started the tree's story; the telling of my stories, through the tree and through me. Yes, I was hooked and needed to learn more about this tree. Why? Why has this tree ignited such a profound effect on me? There's no way for us to know why, but I had to know more. I am completely and utterly amazed at how this one encounter with this one tree has pulled pages from my life, stories that were locked away in the vault of my being. They were now set free through the weeping willow tree, through me, and to you.

One night, tossing and turning, fighting with my pillow, my mind was full of questions. Sleep was not going to happen, so I sat up in bed and just looked at the four walls. The only thing to do now was to get up. Since the computer was in another room of the house, and I didn't want to wake anyone else up, I tip-toed very quietly to the room that housed the computer. I turned it on, ready for information about the weeping willow trees hoping that it might clear up my thoughts a little. What I found was extraordinary. Trees are wonderful, and we certainly don't appreciate what they do for us. Just think about it. Standing high above everything around it, majestic in all his beauty. One of nature's great breathtaking wonders for all to see. Yes, there is beauty everywhere in the world of weeping willow trees.

The tree stands out, not knowing why. You will find the tree alone looking over the horizon, branches hanging low, searching, hoping, and weeping for a life misunderstood. A life that forever would not be and could not be. Weeping willow thought everything would be different if only he was human. If only, yes, if only. Weeping Willow shakes a little and leaves fall to the ground as he daydreams about his misfortune. Weeping Willow tree has grown so big and tall over the years. Reaching upward, high towards the sky, swaying back and forth, and remembering. Life is so full of people and their many adventures. The tree has been honored to witness and hear a few. Weeping Willow smiles to himself thinking about the many stories he could tell. Come on. Take this journey with us. You might see yourself or someone you know. One of the stories just might touch your heart in some way and change your perspective on life. It's a roller coaster ride all the way, with twists and turns that will excite your imagination and your curiosity that will leave you eager to read on. You will be held in the grip of these intriguing stories as they are surely thought-provoking and entertaining. The next page begins our first story. Read on and be helped in experience, reflection, and great knowledge. Even though it feels like a fantasy to me, maybe because I believe in fairy tales, it is still very much reality. See you in the pages of this great book for now and forever.

STORY ONE

THE BEGINNING

The beginning of the weeping willow story started out about one tree's encounter with one person. Me. The book has taken on a life of its own. Weeping Willow - the book, has evolved into an abundance of stories about true-life events that the tree was destined to be a part of. Everyday happenings that intertwine with, and could be, your story. As I stated before, nothing was in my world or mind regarding the weeping willow tree. The trees can be found in or near watery areas. Most are found in the forest, but if you are lucky, one may be found near you.

On many trips out and about, I have passed the trees in parks, on house-lined streets, and picnic areas. The trees were there always watching as we laughed, talked, ate our food, and drank in merriment. There they stood in many different sizes, shapes, and beautiful arrays of color in shades of green shared for all to see. To me, they were just trees, not giving them a second thought. Then one day, on one of the many excursions my students and I ventured into, we turned a corner onto a beautiful roadway, not sure where we were headed. I glanced to my right and there it was. I couldn't say a word. Me, speechless. In front of me was the most magnificent, jaw-dropping tree I've ever seen. I got out of the vehicle, walked over to the weeping willow tree, and stood there just looking up at it. "Wow!"

On the day, the Weeping Willow tree captured something in my spirit. When I touched it, I had the feeling of being touched by a part of the universe. A part that had longed to be discovered. A part of me, a voice silenced, now free to speak. Now, not afraid. We connected. Really, it is a mystery to me, and I cannot describe or fully explain it to you all. But I'll let you be the judge.

There you have it. The beginning of my story, Weeping Willow's story. Tucked away in the crevice of my mind now released to the world.

It is crazy, yet captivating. I have seen many trees. Why this one and why now? The tree evoked a feeling of, "I know you; I feel you." I was so overwhelmed in the moment, caught up in something greater than me. Weeping Willowing tree, an amazing, inspiring wonder, has truly mesmerized me with its branches drooping toward the Earth. I stepped back a little, looked up again at the tree, and asked the question. My reasons for asking? I don't know.

"Oh! Great Weeping Willow, why are you weeping? You are so massive and appear so strong. Yet you stand here and weep."

The tree shook a little. Dew fell to the Earth, expressing the tree's sadness. "Don't ask me." Though I understood what I needed to do, the "why" was a mystery to me. I feel it though. Yeah. Weeping Willow, I will write your story. The world must hear it. The world will no longer wonder. They will know why.

All-day I had a feeling of anticipation. Something wonderful was about to happen. As soon as I got home, my hands were needing to hold a pen, put it to paper, and let the writing commence. I have a computer, but I could not type as fast as I could write. The words came pouring out of me onto the paper. My hands moved by a force that took control. I could not stop. For hours and days, I wrote. One story, two stories, and so on. The stories are from the computer in my mind, yet they were there the whole time.

Maybe, I just needed the weeping willow's permission to start. Weeping Willow drove me to do a project that I had no idea was in me. Who? Me? Bring something to the people of the world? Adventures to repeat, again and again. Read on and you will understand.

STORY TWO

It's Only Whipped Cream

Hmmm. Who is this young man coming up the dirt road? The young man looks familiar. He reminds me of someone. He shared a story with me not so long ago. The tree went back in time, wanting to tell the young man's story. Remember, remember. It is becoming clearer to me now.

The young man is back home from college to visit his family and friends for the holidays. It was always such a joy for him to come home. Que was his name and he knew everyone would be waiting for him. He was their shining star and hero. The entire family loved hearing about his many adventures at school. The family would have to wait, Que also wanted to visit his friend of not-so-long-ago. A certain tree. In the young man's memory, the tree brings so much joy and listens to his stories. He had shared many with the tree during his growing up to adulthood. He felt better after venting under the tree and sorting out life's questions. Que was named after one of his grandfather's brothers. He looked up at the tree smiling, thinking about the story he was about to tell.

Here is one for you, Weeping Willow. The last time I was here to visit you and my family, a funny thing occurred. At least I thought it was funny. You be the judge. Here it is from start to finish.

The young man smiled and pulled his coat tight around him.

Are you ready?

The tree shook a little as a cool wind breezed through the tree's branches.

My college mate and I talked about going home for weeks for the holidays. Weeping Willow, we had the best holiday you can imagine. I mean ever. Everything was perfect. It did not disappoint us. Oh! I am getting ahead of myself. Back to us getting to the airport. There were so many people going home or somewhere. It made our hearts warm a little bit to see the wonder of Christmas in action. Yes, to witness such an exodus home, people trying to get to their loved ones. Traveling from all corners of the world. Wow!

"Lance, we are a part of it!" I told him.

Lance and I were so excited about the spirit of Christmas, we were caught up in it too. We smiled at everyone with cheerful greetings, "Happy holidays, merry Christmas and a happy new year."

Our complete trip was going so smoothly.

Weeping Willow found this difficult to believe as Que explained how on one occasion, he forgot all the presents he was going to bring with him and another time Lance forgot what time their plane was leaving.

Stepping on the plane for home, our anticipation was at full tilt. Man! You just don't know how long I have been wanting good home cooking. after surviving on pasta for so long and other delicacies that I will not mention at this time. I had to tell Lance the treat he was in for.

Let me tell you, Lance, my mom never lets anyone down when it comes to cooking. Mom's entire family can cook and they always receive compliments from anyone lucky enough to sample their foods. Mom said she hung around to watch and learn whenever one of her parents was throwing down in the kitchen cooking. They could make those pots and pans talk! It was as if you were at a cooking symphony being orchestrated by them. It was so beautiful to watch. The aromas, a pleasure to any heart and soul. Think man, in a short time I will be enjoying all those delicious dishes.

"Man! I can't wait!"

"Lance, you are welcome to come over anytime," I told him as I buckled my seat belt. We looked out the window, eager to take off. "I get the window seat!" Lance chimed in. Time for departure. I love to fly, anywhere, anytime. Yeah. During the flight, I handed a card to Lance. I wanted him to see how much I was looking forward to going home. I wrote a little something for my mother on this card. I love people to know how I feel about my family, about home. Home is always there for me. I will tell you a secret. It is where I go to regroup from all the troubles of the world. It was a resume from my heart.

"This day is special. It is special because it represents 30 years of knowing you, 30 years of learning from you, 30 years of your protection, and the exact number of your undying, unwavering love. 30 years is a long time and I hope within these 30 years I have grown into a man you are supremely proud of. I hope within these 30 years I have done right by the life you have given me. I am a lucky man. I am lucky because so many people

do not have a clue what true "love" is. Jesus/God's love. The kind of love that is void of judgment; it is pure. But I do. You. You have shown me this love every waking moment of my life. I still have an unopened present with your love inside. You have been my example for 30 years. I could not have been more blessed. I love you to no end."

"Wow!" Lance's eyes filled with tears. "It is beautiful, Que."

Lance turned his head and looked out the window for a short time. He was quiet, absorbing the words on the paper.

"Man! You are lucky and blessed."

"You know the apple doesn't fall far from the tree," I said.

We both laughed. I told him how my mom was always saying to me, you make my heart smile.

"Your mom is going to cherish this card forever," Lance said.

I agreed with him. I knew she would. We would be home soon and I was excited to give it to her. We raised our hands in the air, not interested in who was watching us and enjoyed the rest of the flight.

As soon as we arrived, the party began. We were ready for a wonderful stay with family and friends. We stayed up all night playing games and watching the television. I have to say it, we played those video games for hours and hours. We even had my father hooked on playing with us. You know how you can set up your system and play with people all over the world? That's what we did and it was awesome. We slept all day to be ready and rested for the nightlife that was waiting for us. No worries at home, ever. Everyone was calling and texting each other as to what our next activity on the agenda was. Lance and my family knew each other for years. We grew up together so it was natural for us to party together. The guys all got together and went out to the movies or out to dinner for some guy time. It was time for nightlife. All the guys got dressed to go out dancing. Man did we all look sharp! We arrived at the club and it was in full swing. The music was loud and energetic. This is what we came for. It's true about the ladies loving a college man. They were all over us. Not once, all evening, did we leave the dance floor. I loved it. All my friends joined in. We all loved it. We had a great time; the evening went perfectly. We needed this night to just let go. Man! And we did.

After two weeks of sheer happiness, it was time to go back to school. I love it at the University, so it was no problem that we were going back. The dorm I live in is a home away from home. We had friends there that cared about us plus we always put education first. Our bags were packed and full of new items to take back with us. Lance's parents dropped him off at my house so they could wave hello to my parents. We said our goodbyes to everyone. My father offered to take us to the airport. We loaded our bags in the trunk of the car and we were off. My dad is an excellent driver and made sure we were always safe and got to our destination. That is my dad. We knew all the guys would want to hear all about our trip home. I always would bring special treats for them. We wanted to take some of our good times and share them. Just a little piece of it. This visit was no exception.

Weeping Willow, you will not believe what happened on our way to the airport. We decided to stop at one of the great restaurants in the area and get some sweets from there. That place is known for their desserts. We decide on delicious pies to take back with us.

"Dad, do you want a pie?" I asked him.

"No, thank you. Your mom had quite a spread for us, this morning. I am still feeling the love." We all laughed at his reply.

There was no parking in the lot when we arrived, so my father let me out at the front entrance. I jumped out of the car feeling like a million dollars. Upon entering the restaurant, two cashiers greeted me.

"Can we help you?" asked the second cashier.

"Yes," I replied.

The first cashier stepped forward, "I can help you."

"I want two pies to go."

"Of course."

As I went to make my selection, I noticed that the flavor of pies I wanted had whipped cream about one inch thick on it. I explained to the cashier that I wanted that flavor of pie, just without the whipped cream.

"Oops, sorry. No one informed me that we do not have any of those pies without whipped cream on them."

Cashier 1 turned to cashier 2. "Why didn't someone tell me that most of the pies have whipped cream on them?"

"I am just starting my shift." Cashier 2 said defensively. "And do not yell at me in that harsh tone!" she added.

Personally, it did not sound like yelling to me, but apparently, there was something else going on. It was quiet for a moment as they looked at each other. I spoke up.

"I don't want whipped cream everywhere. I am taking a flight out of here as soon as I get those pies. Can one of you just clean the whipped cream off of the pie?"

Cashier 2 rushed over, "I will do it."

She started to shave off the pie with the skill of a fine surgeon.

"I do not want to make any holes in the pie," she explained.

Cashier 1 had another idea about the best way to clean the pie. Nonetheless, Cashier 2 kept her attention on getting all the whipped cream off the pie and did not acknowledge Cashier 1. There was a little tension in the air. At that moment, my college friend came in.

"Man! We are going to miss our flight. What is taking so long?"

I pointed to Cashier 2 trying to get the whipped cream off the pie.

"What?" he asked, confused.

"I will tell you about it later," I explained.

I looked at Cashier 2.

"I need to go. Can you please just take a napkin and finish the pie? Thank you," I said in a calm quiet voice. I did not want to upset anyone.

Again, cashier 1 started to say something to cashier 2, but the look on 2's face warned 1 against it. It stopped Cashier1 dead in their tracks. Cashier 1 looked at us, lifted their shoulders, turned, and walked away.

Cashier 2 smiled at us. "Your pies are ready. Here you go."

I took the pies and headed towards the door.

"You guys have a safe trip." Words from both of the cashiers.

We hurried out the door.

"Good Grief! It was only whipped cream. We have a flight to catch," I expressed to Lance.

We ran to the car and we got in.

"Did you guys make the pies?" My father asked sarcastically.

"Almost," I replied. We all laughed.

My thoughts went back to the restaurant as I rested my head on the headrest, as we drove toward our destination. I was thinking of the cashiers. They were very friendly toward us, the customer. Yet, to each other, they were rude. Life is too short, Weeping Willow. We can't sweat the small stuff. We must remember to communicate with our co-workers, or with anyone we have a misunderstanding with. It is very important to talk it over. Do not hold anything in or it will fester and become out of control. Get a clear understanding of what the other person is trying to convey. Listen, it is key and be willing to forgive. You will see in the big picture of life. It is nothing to get all out of sorts about. We all just want to be happy wherever we are. Life is so simple when you just let go and not sweat the small stuff. Weeping Willow, it's time for me to go. I have so much to give out there in this big beautiful world of ours.

The young man stood up, touched the tree, and smiled.

It was only whipped cream.

He nodded gently, turned, and walked away. In a split second, he was gone.

STORY THREE

Highway 4 Angel

Do you believe in angels? There is no doubt in my mind that they exist. There are many reasons to believe in angels. We don't think about it, but they walk beside us every day. Here is a story about one of them. I do not know who or where you are, but I hope you know that you are an angel.

Today is the day I have been waiting for. I am off from work, taking a much-needed break. My job can be very physically and mentally challenging, but I work hard and I love it. I feel needed and have a purpose in this world. My students love me, and I love them. Nonetheless, everyone needs a day off.

On this day, shopping was the only agenda on my mind when I woke up this glorious morning. Birds were singing in the trees near my unique, breathtaking view from my window. My bed faced the front of the window. I wanted to catch a peek at the birds that lived in the trees or the many beautiful ones that would fly by. There were so many, each featuring all the colors of nature. Many mornings, the birds woke me up with their singing. It was lovely. You live for a minute like this one when you feel totally free without a care in the world. I felt like a baby on a cloud, floating and wrapped in pillowy softness.

My laundry was done the day before, everything smelled so fresh. I had the feeling of being in a field of fresh scented flowers, on a hillside with a breeze blowing ever so gently, spreading the perfume aroma everywhere. It was difficult for me to get up. My blankets were velveted and so soft to the touch. I stretched my whole body, from head to toes. So good! My husband had been extremely sweet and attentive the day before. The memory of it made me curl up in a ball, like a kitten with a toy. I smiled. It was a great day to be alive. All was right in the world. Life is so good.

I daydream as I think about getting out of bed. "Oh! Time to move." The sun was shining big and bright in the sky. As I opened the window, the rays touched my face like warm heat from my blow dryer. How sweet and wonderful it felt. What a day this is going to be. There were so many positive signs. The summer was almost over. We did not know how many days we were going to have like this one. My goal was to have as much fun that I could, like always. You see, shopping and I have a love affair going on. In other words, I love to shop. I am known for my shopping. I love to spend that money! Plans for the day were mapped out ahead of time.

"Let's get started," I spoke out loud as I jumped into the shower.

After my shower, I lounged around in my pink plush robe, one of my favorite colors. I love feeling soft and cozy; so, I wrapped the robe snuggly around me. Nice. My clothes were already picked, thank goodness because I didn't want to think about what to wear. I have so many clothes, sometimes it's difficult to decide. Though, I'm not bragging. I work long hours to get what I want and it wasn't always like this. Anyways, my clothes were draped on a chair in my bedroom. Now all I had to do was slip them on.

"Girl! You look good!" I said to myself as I looked at my reflection.

I opted for something small and light for breakfast. Anything too heavy would slow me down and I didn't want any interference that day. Toast and juice was just enough.

So, I hit the road and was on my way.

It is a treat to go visit other towns and cities to shop. We visit their stores, eat at the many restaurants, and taste sweet and delicious foods from all over the world. We drive miles from home. It makes us all feel connected.

The mall was crowded, people everywhere. I love it when it is like this. I feel everything is alright with the world and am glad to be a part of it. There was no reason to hurry back home. Everyone was busy with tasks, yet here I was, free to roam, and just be me. Yeah, it felt so good I started with the perfume shop. Perfumes from all over the world surrounded me and I loved it! Smelling them can take me to different countries around the world. France is one of my favorite cities to dream about. It is said to be one of the most romantic cities in the world. It might be true especially if you are with the one you love.

Sitting in front of the tree, Kitty smiled to herself.

"Believe me, I know," she said, responding to her own statement and clearly carrying a special secret that only she knows.

"Someday, I will get there in person," she vowed before continuing her story.

There were food samples in many of the stores to enjoy, and I did. My tummy was getting so full. It was definitely time to stop. I had to tell myself, "Kitty you do not have to sample everything today. Just look and enjoy the sights. There will be other days for sure." I looked into many windows and after a little walking, it was time to try on clothes. I absolutely love modeling clothes. Oh! And we can't forget the shoes. I love, love shoes! Usually, after trying on many pairs, I might buy two or more pairs if they hit me just right. Life is so good to me. More walking, and after going back and forth the length of the mall, I stopped.

"What is next?" I asked aloud

Right in front of me, as I turned, was something that greatly excited me. I was standing face to face with a spa. Wow! How could I forget about the spa? A manicure and pedicure sounded great right. It would feel so good to sit and relax after all that shopping. Yes indeed, I needed it. My hands were full of clothes, shoes, and bags. My feet did not hurt at all in my new shoes. The worst thing to happen when shopping is for your feet to hurt. I've learned my lesson and now I wear easy shoes when shopping. It's no fun for any part of your body to hurt.

Upon entering the spa, the clerk asked, "Can I help you?"

"Yes, please. A mani- and a pedicure," I answered.

I wanted to feel the warm water between my toes. I submerged my feet in the warm bath. It felt great. I leaned back in the chair which seemed to be made of leather. The chair was warm and hugged me like an old friend who was glad to see me. I closed my eyes and started to reminisce about friends not being here with me.

Yes, we shopped together on many adventures. I can see their faces smiling with such joy. We all shop in different ways, hurried or very calm. We all care about each other too. It is a wonderful life to have true friends and we feel the void when one of us is missing in action. The women are strong intelligent women with high-paying jobs. They are also involved in many causes, always helping people and giving back to the community. Paying it forward. They shop to relieve some of their stress and because they love it. I am not saying they don't love their jobs. They do. It's just that each of us needs to shake off the day's problems and just relax and do whatever makes us happy. Many outfits show off their personalities. Expensive to the everyday casual. Yes, we have a great time together sharing our lives. We're also very competitive. We often share our victories in sports, each one of us placing ourselves in any sports arena overcoming every obstacle to take our opponent down. Game night was always wild and we always caused a scene.

We had many parties. Such great parties. They were always exceptional. Uh-huh! We shimmied and danced the night away. It was always up for debate who had the best moves. We were all outstanding dancers, well, depending on who lasted the longest in our high heels. We outdid ourselves on the dance floor. Ok, the truth is, we took our shoes off sometimes, but we'd never tell anyone.

Homelife was good. Not perfect but good. All of us did everything in our power to make sure our homes ran as smoothly as possible. We all know there will be rainy days and sunny days in our lives. When life events came up, we each dealt with them with understanding and tried not to sweat the small stuff. In the big picture of life, you will see that most of the things we carry on about don't matter at all. We try to live a simple life and stress less.

Anyways, I love being with my friends, but today I was shopping alone. By choice. Shopping was so much fun, finding bargain after bargain. Yeah, I am good. I am really good.

Once the nail technician finished, I looked at my watch. I did not realize it was so late. It was time to head home. The mall was still crowded with many shoppers looking, searching, or just not ready to go home and enjoying themselves. The second I exited the building, I noticed how dark it had gotten. In the mall, you can so easily lose track of time. So much to do and see. Luckily, my car was easy to find. I always park in the same area of the mall. I don't like to be one of those people who can't find their car. They have a lost and confused look on their faces. Nonetheless, my car was a little farther than I remembered. But there it was, near the back of the lot. I rushed to it with all my bags, so happy to be going home with all my prizes. It was a great day to do anything. It was still warm outside. I started to sing as I put all my bags in the car. I turned on the radio and one of my favorite songs was playing. You just don't know how I felt. A natural high. "Fantastic" is one word that would describe how wonderful I was feeling. Exiting the parking lot was easy, people were still hanging out in the mall so there was no traffic jam to deal with. "Awesome" was all I could think.

I headed for the freeway: Highway 4. It will take me all the way home. It was dark on Highway 4. I attempted to turn on my headlights. Nothing.

"What is wrong?" I asked myself out loud. "Wait a minute, maybe I am a little tired."

I tried to turn them on again. Still nothing. I passed the last exit and tried again to make the lights work. They would not come on so I flashed my high beams. It was very dark now and I couldn't see anything. I couldn't believe it. Luckily, there were no cars on the freeway. (Not that I would have stopped.) I turned my high beams on and off trying to figure out what was going on with my lights. Wow! This was dangerous stuff. I was totally confused as to what was going on but I couldn't pull over. It was too dark. I didn't know what would happen if I kept going. I started to get very frightened.

"Keep calm, get control of yourself," I told myself.

Suddenly, lights appeared in my rearview mirror. I could pull over, but I was too nervous. If only I was where there was a little light and a few other people. Man! The moon was not out that night either. The car in the rear could tell I was in trouble and confused about what was going on with my car. I was driving a normal speed, yet they did not go around me. Instead, they kept their lights on to guide my way. They lit up the night for me and did not leave me alone. They were with me all the way to the end of Highway 4. As I entered the intersection, the car went around me and honked their horn. Even though I was still very upset about the situation, I wondered. Who was in that car? They didn't stop and they made sure I was safe. "Goodbye, my Angel." Then they were gone.

I continued home with my high beams on. I did not have far to go. Entering home, I broke down and started to cry. I could not hold it in any longer. My husband and daughter were at home and ran to console me.

"What's the matter?" they both asked at the same time.

"I could have been killed on Highway 4. My car lights refused to come on," I explained. I turned to my daughter. *"You had my car for a couple of days. Did you know that the lights would not come on?"*

"Sorry, mom. I didn't know you were going to take the car."

"It's ok, I am safe now. Please, next time let me know. I understand you are a new driver, but you must take responsibility for the car you are driving especially when things go wrong.".

I do not know who you are or where you are. Thank you again and keep protecting people like me. My Highway 4 Angel. I love you.

The next day, Kitty took off for one of her favorite places to be. Under a great weeping willow tree. She shared her life with this tree. The tree knew her well. Her ups and downs. Her good times and bad times. The tree was always there to listen. Kitty loved trees, but this one was special. She could hardly wait to tell the tree what happened the day before. As Kitty approached the tree, she stopped to catch her breath.

I ran all the way here, she explained to Weeping Willow

Kitty placed her hand on the tree and leaned on it as she eased her way to the base of the tree.

Wow! That feels good,"

With a sigh of relief first, Kitty repeated her story to the tree. Crying a little here and there, trying to share the story clearly. After a while, she was quiet, looking out, over and beyond the area of the tree, thinking to herself. Suddenly, she spoke again.

Somewhere out there, I have an angel. I am so lucky to be alive and well to enjoy this beautiful day with you. I almost forgot. I brought you a little something."

Kitty dug a little hole under the tree. She placed small sticks of fertilizer in the soil around the tree.

Hope you like it. Kitty smiled big; I was thinking of you.

Kitty stayed with the tree for hours, sitting, and being at peace with herself and the world. As darkness started to slowly creep in, Kitty jumped up.

Time to go. You know I will return another day.

Kitty touched the tree one more time letting her hand linger for an extra second. She walked up the pathway, turned, and waved once more at the tree, then she was gone.

Story Three Poetry

"THE GIFT"

Nature did not promise that life would be perfect always.
There are many ups and downs in
this gift that was given to each of us
Life.
Rainy days and stormy days
but the sun will come out for sure.
Unexpected
Your headlights, so bright, lit my way.
There will be pain and sorrow.
Look around you.
Do not fear. I am here
look in your rear-view mirror.
When we open our hearts
Love is there.
There is peace and joy.
Be at ease. I am safe.
At the end of the night
I see stoplights.
You loved me. "Yeah, and I am Grateful."

STORY FOUR

WHAT IS THE MEANING OF LIFE?

As usual, Weeping Willow tree was looking out surveying the area beyond him, thinking how lucky he is to live in such a beautiful place. A car drove up going very fast. Screech!!

We passed the tree. Go back!

The car stopped at the path leading up to the tree. Four young men jump out of the fancy car.

"Everything has changed around here," one of the young men shouted out.

They all look in the direction of the tree.

See you guys. Didn't I tell you this tree is something special?"

All the young men just stare at the tree for a few minutes. They could not move at first, not farther than the pathway.

"Man! You were not kidding. It is magnificent. When you would talk about this place, we were a little skeptical of the stories you told. It just did not seem real. Now we believe. We believe!"

After a short while, they collected themselves and walked in the direction of the tree, taking long steps. One of the young men stretched out his arms.

Look, Tree! It's me, Justice! I have come back to visit you, Weeping Willow. Remember? I told you I would return. Here are three of my best friends. Mighty Mike, Reynaldo, and Sal. I have told them much about you, Weeping Willow. Here I am, all grown up and handsome. Don't you guys all agree?

"Yeah, in your dreams," one of them said and they all laughed.

one of them said and they all laughed. *We want to share something with you. Life has been good to all of us so far. Yet, we all feel there is something missing.*

Weeping Willow recognized the young man. He was one of the children that played here. He is the one always doing drama or play-acting of some sort. "Practice, practice" the young boy would say many times. "Someday I am going to be a famous actor and star in many plays and movies." The young boy would take a bow. "I can hear the applause. I love the theater, I come alive. It's fantastic to take people to another place, another time. Wow! I would love to bring such joy to others," he would say. Weeping Willow shook and leaves fell to the ground in honor of this young man. He is the one with a big gorgeous smile, an amazing voice, and such a charming personality. He was unbelievably kind to the other children.

That is so very funny that I remember those things about him. All good attributes to carry through life. Yes, he gave me and the children many hours of entertainment and laughter. Well, here he is all grown up and bringing friends to visit me.

The tree was so delighted with Justice and his friends. This made the tree very glad. There had been so much negativity blowing through the tree coming from the world beyond. Justice not only came back himself but brought friends who are also doing well in their lives.

You just don't know.

Weeping Willow moved his branches from side to side creating a cool breeze for the young men.

Justice started to speak and leaned against the tree. The other young men followed and touched the tree.

Can we rest here under your cool branches? We need to discuss the information given to us. Our heads and minds are full. We have been all over the world. We have spoken to many people and we have gotten many different answers. We are searching and seeking the meaning of life. Can someone tell us? Through many cities and towns, states, and countries we've traveled. Everyone we interviewed, on mountain tops, in ships on the seas, in valleys high and low, we repeated the question, "What is the meaning of life?" We got so many answers. We needed to go over the advice we received. Much of it is a little different yet the same. Maybe if we blend them all together, we can agree on something so simple and great. We'll read many of the statements from people, family, and friends.

The young men pulled out pieces of paper with words written on them. They agreed to take turns reading them out loud. Justice, who lived for speaking and was destined to be a leader, naturally went first.

"Live your life with empathy and compassion."

"Love is the greatest gift of all."

"Stay healthy, eat green apples, lemons, and cucumbers."

"Fear nothing, it can paralyze you."

"Stay in your lane."

"Be Kind."

"Help others."

"Be humble, but fierce. Birds of a feather flock together. Do not flock with birds who have ruffled feathers."

"Follow your own yellow brick road."

"Do not venture into places you do not know."

"Move."

"Don't give up, Ever."

"Have meaning and purpose."

"Find joy in the simple everyday things."

"Choose your friends wisely."

"Be grateful."

"Love what you do."

"Stay healthy."

"Remember, everything in moderation."

"Have mercy and be merciful."

"Stay in peace."

"Make an effort, then see what happens."

"Let love in your life."

"Blessed are the pure of heart."

"Eat to live, not live to eat."

"Love, it rules the universe."

"Get plenty of sleep next to someone who loves you."

"The eyes don't lie."

"Seek and you will find."

"Be the change you want to see in others."

"Smile."

"Be still and know God."

"To see yourself in the faces of your children."

"Do what you can."

"Listen well and understand."

"Be a peacemaker."

"Hope, joy, peace cometh in the morning."

"Don't carry around extra baggage, let it go."

"Forgive."

"Celebrate life."

"Express yourself."

"Share your love and kindness with others."

"Live with integrity and respect."

"Peace of mind."

"Love."

"The grass is not always greener on the other side."

"All money is not good money."

"Break bad habits."

"Don't bite the hand that feeds you."

"Take time to smell the roses of life."

"Be joyful of mind and spirit."

"Cleanliness is next to nature."

"Do unto others as you would have them do unto you."

"A bird in the hand is worth ten in the bush."

"Slow down."

"Leave footprints in the sand beside you."

"You are not alone."

"Stress less."

"Everyone needs standards to live by."

"Don't give up on your dreams."

"Always think before you act."

"There is a logical explanation for everything."

"Learn from your mistakes, follow a different path."

"Quiet time is to sort out the YouTube in your mind."

"Try, try and try again if you need to."

"An ounce of prevention is worth a truck load of cures."

"Health, happiness, and love of family."

"Give back to the world."

"Material things have no real value."

"Get your own."

"Enjoy the beauty around you."

"Make something of yourself."

"Freedom."

"Be a rock for someone."

"Salvation, once you have that, you have everything."

"Come in out of the rain."

"Know who you are."

"See no evil, hear no evil, speak no evil."

"I want to live."

"Do the right thing, then you will not have to worry about a thing."

"Everyone must make a choice, develop your own discipline in a world where everything goes."

"You will reap what you sow."

"Respect the guardians of the universe, they take care of us all."

*"Respect the animals that gives us much,
they guide, but we don't see.
They live and die by the laws of nature."*

Can you believe this? All of us attended Universities, colleges, and many other fields of study and endeavors. We have traveled all over the world to come back to my mother where we started out in life. We asked her the question. "Mom, what is the meaning of life?"

She smiled and said, "It is so simple. You carry it with you everywhere. Young men, listen. The meaning of life is knowing how to use what you have, and all good things will come to you. Know how to give love and receive love. Use it well and all the treasures of life will come to you. Understand your mate, your match. You only need one, the right one.

Seek and you shall find. The laws of nature are set. Bend them a little you can try. It drives the universe."

My *mom smiled again." I* could have told you years ago but you had to be ready to receive it. You guys had to go on a quest for yourselves to see what you might find. Life is similar to a book; every chapter is different. Do not stop in the middle of the book. Read on and in the end, you might be surprised."

We all looked at each other, not sure of what to make of what we just heard. We walked away with a puzzled look as we tried to process my mom's theory on the meaning of life. But before we stepped out the door, the wise guru gave us more words of wisdom, but this time it was on a handwritten letter.

Justice pulled a folded piece of paper from his pocket, opened it, and began to read aloud.

"Love is as deep and everlasting as the stars in the night sky. It is written and so shall it be for now and always that I love you. Many stories have been told and written about love. Our story is one of them. Ok. Let me try to describe what I want to convey another way and I hope you understand the relationship between your father and me. It's a man and woman thing. Someday you will know. When I first saw your father, I knew he was the man for me. A woman knows immediately when that's him. There he was, my knight in all his glory, dancing and smiling. The man I had waited for, longed for. He had the body of a strong warrior, a gladiator. His smile penetrated my heart and made me tremble. I didn't see the dents in his armor at that moment, not that it would have mattered. Everyone has something in their past. My heart had been pierced with the arrow of cupid.

This man was all I could see. As it shall be, he walked over to me. "Would you like to dance?" There was nothing I could do or wanted to do but run into his arms. It felt so good. Here was my destiny and I reveled in it. From that day to this one, we never parted. I knew that love passed my way and consumed me. Our life was filled with much love and pleasure. All that was in him to give he gave to me. And it was good! I was blessed to have him. He gave me the two of you. How to convey to you how I feel about the main man in my home. He gave me fire; he gave me passion. He gave me quiet moments to sort out the YouTube in my mind. I felt safe and protected with him. I could be at peace with him. Be myself with him. Love can be as delicate as a flower. Love can be as gentle as an angel's kiss. Love can be as violent and roaring as the ocean waves. Love can bring kings to their knees. Love can bring queens to kings. Love can rule a heart and a kingdom. Love can be enduring as life itself. Love can be peaceful. Love is home, this is where I belong. The circle of his arms. The touch of his lips on ripe lips waiting for the tender kiss. Love can humble you. Love is looking into your eyes not having to say a word, knowing what the other is thinking. Love is a smile that sets your body ablaze with passion. Love, oh love. I hope you can capture this feeling once in your lifetime. The animalistic chemistry of 'I want you, only you. Let me give you what you have been waiting for.' Yes, oh yes! My sweets, this love will carry you through the ups and downs that will surely come. You will tackle them together. Memories, if you can imagine, that your body and mind will store in a computer bank forever. Only that touch and that alone can ignite all you know of love. You can find true love that will last a lifetime if you believe. He stated in every way, 'You embrace me with more than arms alone.' Feel the heat from the smile on my face as I remember him and his words to me. Should I seek more that time has passed by? No. Camelot was mine and it was wonderful. Love, mom."

Justice returned the paper to his pocket and continued to reminisce.

Remember, another wise Guru spoke with us at length about getting married. He said, "Young men, marriage is a great commitment. Do not take it lightly. It is one of the greatest joys with the right person. It is work, but it is so worth it. It is one of the biggest decisions you will make in this life. What is, prenuptial? Society has put this word in our thought process and confused us in dealing with our partners. What is important in this life? Do not be distracted. Follow the laws of nature. You change the dynamic of a relationship when you use those words, 'pre-nuptial'. You do not know it, but you confuse her. Women do not go into a relationship thinking, I am going to take all the money. If a woman cares for you and wants you she will go to the ends of the Earth for you. Young men, if a woman decides to mate with you, it is special. She has chosen you above all others. A woman will give you all that is in her power to give to you that has been ordained by nature. It may not seem like much in this day and age, nonetheless, it is too powerful. It rules everything. An empty house can be very cold and lonely. All the money in the world will not keep you warm in the winter. You chose. Most women want to know that if she gave her heart away, you would take care of her and your children and not abuse them. Women need love and affection. Take her and hold her tight and never let go. She will never leave you. Young men, build a strong foundation in your relationship that is solid. Cherish her and kiss her. Have you heard the saying, it's in the kiss? In return, she will take care of you. We all know there are exceptions to every rule. If you are fair and honest about whatever is going, all will be well. Remember, your children suffer the most in times of trouble. Think about everything you do, weigh every option. Man is a seeker and a conqueror. He will go out from time to time, wandering but he will tire and return home. She will be waiting. She will let you rest. Feed you if you are hungry. Rub your tired body. You will know that she is always there for you. This is where you belong. Home with me. "Now sleep, my love," she says to him as she kisses him on the cheek.

With all the advice that was given to us, I knew just the place to go and sort all this out. So here we are under my friend, Weeping Willow Tree.

I understand what my mother was trying to say to us about life. It is all so clear now.

They all looked at each other and started to crack-up. For a few minutes, they found it hard to stop!

Ok. Ok. Get it under control. We all have decisions to make and start living our lives to the fullest. What one of my uncles said, have a good mate beside you. A person to share the good times and bad times, who understands you and accepts you for who you are, not what they think you should be. In other words, someone who always has your back.

The guys all looked at each other. "Yeah."

So there the men sat and discussed, they pondered and debated until finally, they reached a decision.

We each must find our own path. What makes each one of us happy.

They all agreed.

Man, I feel so good. We have accomplished so much under this tree.

The young men stood up and patted the tree.

Do you agree with that, Weeping Willow?

All the young men laughed and gave a sigh of relief from their search. Each one of them now had the answer to their meaning of life.

Mighty Mike rubbed his stomach "I am hungry. Let's get something to eat. All this discussion and mind stirring conversation, we need to eat." Reynaldo and Sal agreed that they too were starving.

"Man! I could eat a large steak right now," Justice chimed in. "And I know just the place to go."

The young men walked down the path, turned once more toward the tree, and gave a silent thank you.

I told you guys the tree was something special.

The young men all agreed. "Yes!" They jumped in the car, then they were gone.

Here are a few simple words of wisdom from Weeping Willow tree to you...

Adoration from people leaves me so humble. Many stories have come across these branches from many people about their journeys through life. People come and go throughout the years. Some return again and again, many do not. I hope their many adventures were safe and they are living their lives to the peak of happiness. I hope all their searches and wishes have materialized. Hmm mm, yes, to love and be loved.

The tree shook a little.

Each of us has a time to be here on this great Earth. Find your purpose and passion. Waste no time wishing and hoping. You have got to get up and move. Time waits on no man. It is fleeting, so quickly it goes by. Cherish the small things in life. Stop and smell the roses of life. Take your time. Smile and share your happiness with others. Do not sweat the small stuff in life. Live in peace and harmony. Life can be wonderful. Remember, if it does not feel right, do not do it. Again, watch the animals. They live and die by the laws of nature. And never forget that life happens.

Story Four Poetry

"I Give"

Here is my heart. Please take it. Appease me.
I give it to you freely without reservation.
Come on walk this land with me.
Hand in hand. We can survive anything.
With you by my side everything is possible.

My heart swells with pride when I think
Of you as my bride.
Life will be so divine knowing you are mine.
You are so fine. Woman you know I love you.

No other is in my heart.
Nothing can keep us apart.
We are one heart beating as one.
"Can you feel it, baby?"
I give my heart to you.
I am ready to consolidate our love.

Believe me, baby, when I say.
You will never regret you chose me.
I will spend my life making you happy.
I am going to take care of you in every way.
Prove to you I am the best man for you.

Here I am
Take me as I am
I give you all of me.
Yours forever.

"A Man In The House"

Men in the house, it is so awesome.
Men make you feel safe and protected.
You sleep good at night, take flight to dreamland.
House feels empty without men in it.
Men make the family whole. My house is not a home
Without my man. Honey came home to me.
I anticipate
Your arrival. Walk through that door.
Let me wrap you in my arms.
Give you what you desire.
All my sweet charms.
Just say the words
I am ready. Feeling you next to me is all I want, all I need.
My man!
It is so good to have you home
No more to roam.
"My man is in the house!"

"Peace Baby Peace"

Peace with you I have found
It is what the world is searching for.
So many people do not know what we know.
Maybe they will find it.
Life is so special to have you.
Love and hold you in the winters of our life.
Warmth is what we need to keep out the cold.
Baby, I look at you and my heart
Is calm and peaceful.
I need to feel the electricity from you to me. "Zap."
Baby, you make me feel so fine all the time.
Let us not waste time.
Your mine.
So divine.
Like a glass of fine wine.
Let me show you how good I treat mine.
Put your head on my shoulder.
And be at peace, baby, peace.

"MY HOME"

It is wonderful to have a place called home.
A place to go when the world has tossed you around.
Took from you all that it could.
Beat you down to the ground.
You are tired of playing the game.
Tired of trying to reach for fame.
Doors being slammed in your face.
The race is yet to be won.
"I just need to rest."
I long for home.
There is peace and quiet.
There is food on the table.
There is a warm smile, hugs, and kisses.
There are gentle words of encouragement.
Truly being loved and
wanted. There is a maze of protection around you.
There is much joy in me.
I realize, "you are my home."

STORY FIVE

THE PROPOSAL

Driving by in a convertible car, also known as a ragtop in the colors of red white, and blue, a young couple sat very close to each other. The young woman's hair was blowing in every direction as the wind whipped through her hair. The tree heard their laughter as they came closer. It was loud, happy, and made you want to join in. Suddenly the car stopped as the young man stepped hard on the brakes hard causing a screeching noise. The car was beautiful. Its wheels shined like a new silver dollar.

Did they feel me? the tree thought in amazement.

The couple got out of the car and stared with their mouths wide open.

"Look at this tree. It's magnificent and beautiful," the couple said in unison.

The young couple walked up the path to Weeping Willow. They were moved to touch the tree.

"I feel something wonderful is about to happen," the young woman blurted out quickly, not knowing why. Perhaps she felt something. In the next moment, the young man started to say something to her.

"Honey, this is perfect. It's the right time, the right place, and I am ready. I want to read something to you that I wrote... It is written in the stars that we should be together. The stars have formed in a lovely pattern just for us to get into our space. Let us accept our fate. There is no time to waste, we should make haste and set a date. I am ready to procreate. It is also written in the stars that I will love you for a million years and throughout time. From the moment I saw you, my heart skipped a beat and I knew. You looked at me. I could do nothing but stare back. Frozen in a world of emotions of anticipated devotion. Only searching your face for a spark of positive emotion. You are the one I have dreamed of. Stayed awake at night thinking of you. Searching for you in many places. Now here you are. My destiny. I want to run, not walk into your arms. Encircle me with your arms and take control of me. I will stroll with you anywhere. I do not want to be alone anymore. I want the warmth of a cozy den with you."

He hesitated a minute to catch his breath after that long speech. Words from his heart. He continued.

"Can I have some water?" he asked.

"Slow down, Kirk. Take your time young man," he said to himself.

But he could not.

"There is only moving forward. My life is yours, all that I have is yours. It is written in the stars and it shall be. Please want me as much as I want you, Candy."

The young man quietly bent down on one knee in front of the young lady and the weeping willow tree as a witness.

"Will you marry me, Candy?" His words came out trembling. "I love you." I want to spend the rest of my life with you."

The young lady was quiet for a moment. She was thinking about all he said. Looking at him with a big smile on her face.

"Are you sure I am what you want? Me, forever? Remember I do not believe in divorce." She was keeping the young man in suspense. "Honey, that was quite a speech you made. I am holding you to it forever."

Again, the young man spoke, "I feel the same way you do." He waited for her answer.

"Ok, let us do it, Kirk. Yes, I will marry you!"

The young couple took each other by the hand. Kirk was so happy, he could not stop talking.

"I did not get the ring yet. I knew you would want to pick it out together."

She looked up at him and smiled. "You know me so well," the young lady said with such emotion.

The tree shook. Weeping Willow felt the emotion., The tree's branches were moving for their happiness. The young couple touched the tree gently.

"Let us carve our names in this great tree to commemorate our union and engagement. Forever." Without any hesitation, Kirk started to carve into the tree.

Ouch! That hurt.

The tree shook gently.

Keep going I do not want you to stop. The pain will be for a short time only.

The tree felt a part of something great and good. Weeping Willow shook again and his leaves fell gently on the couple.

"Look at the leaves falling!" they shouted.

It was clear that the tree approved. They both laughed and bowed to the tree. "Thank you. We will return someday." They took each other's hand, turned, ran to their car. Jumped in and then they were gone.

The tree stood silently watching the couple ride off into the sunset.

Let love rule. You two, this is for you two. Now that you have said yes to the question, "Will you marry me?", you now have eyes for each other only. You felt a tug in your heart and mind that said, 'this is the one.' For life, you will have each other. The work has just begun. Marriage is wonderful. As you two travel alone this highway through life together, there will be lots of twists and turns. Highs and lows. Do not detour. Stay focused on each other. Keep going together. Both of you can make it work and make it very special if you want each other. If you love each other. Remember what makes the other person happy. They had a life before you. Do not try and take it all away. You will not miss your goal of a happy marriage. Always think about why you chose to marry this person. Reflect on it. Do not change the person you are today. Always check yourself. Words of wisdom. Let love rule understanding, compassion, freedom, forgiveness. there will be soft and peaceful moments. But when those moments are not so peaceful, remember to always listen with an open heart, never forget to spend time alone and the most, important thing to remember: do not sweat the small stuff.

Story Five Poetry

"TAKE MY HAND"

Take my hand, walk this life journey with me.
From this day forward
You are my one and only.
Never will I leave you or deceive you.
In my love, you can abide.
We will walk side by side.
I will be your guide through understanding.
Not demanding. Shower you with devotion.
Show my true emotions.
When it is cold, I will cover you.
When it is hot, I will shade you
Shelter you from the rain.
Cause you no pain.
Let you down, never.
If you frown, to make you smile
I will play the clown, I will be here
forever baby.
Forever.

"ABSOLUTELY"

Burning rays of the sun have gone to sleep.
Now in the cool of the evening when the wind
Gently caresses my face as we swing back and forth.
Nestle between two lovely shade trees in a field of green
Shimmering as far as the eyes can see. You hold me firmly
Against your chest and I can hear your beating heart.
I will rest my head on your shoulder and be at peace with you.

"Absolutely."

Happiness came upon me this clear night sparkling
With stars in the sky. This feeling that wrapped around my
heart
Cannot be denied. It is the pride I feel deep in me being with
you
Where I now abide.

"Absolutely."

"JUST RIGHT"

Once in a lifetime.
Once in a lifetime find.
You found me.
It astounds me
We were made for each other.

A cake baked with love, care,
Tenderness and understanding.
Just the right ingredients.
Delicious success to taste
The good life with you.

A love that is right.
You and me tonight.
Nothing can change fate.

A delightful feeling that will not go away.
It affects me in my stomach.
Still feeling it. Remembering in the beginning
When I first laid eyes on you.
That flutter.
I could not utter a word.
You knew what was in my heart

By looking into my eyes to
Reveal what was on my lips to say.
Do not fade away.

I have waited for you for so long.
Now here you are in front of me.
I am too shy to say.
Do not ever go.

STORY SIX

BABY, SWEET BABY

Zoom! Zoom!

Wow! That car is moving fast past me.

Screech!

It's backing up now. Getting out of the car is a lady. She is weeping. She has something in her arms. A beautiful bouquet of fragrant flowers in the colors of red, white, and blue.

The woman slowly walked up the path to the weeping willow tree. She was standing quiet for the longest time. Silent tears cascaded down her cheeks, falling to the ground at the tree's base like big raindrops.

I can taste the tears as they soak into the soil around me where she is standing. They taste like salt crystals, which means she is so, so sad. She bent down and placed the flowers at my base ever so gently. She finally said something.

Oh, great weeping willow tree. My heart is so heavy. My sorrow is almost too much for a person to carry. The days and nights are so long. I weep. I can't think of anything else but him, my sweet baby, sweet baby. He didn't stay very long. He only came for a visit. It was not long enough. Time was not on our side.

I know you wanted to stay. I felt you. "Mommy it's out of my hands. I have done what I was here to do. Now let me go." My baby spoke to me through the universe. I could feel his words in my being. "Don't cry. You were a great mom to me. I felt your love and I will carry it with me throughout time. Hold and kiss me one last time, mommy.

She was beside herself with grief. She begged with everything that was in her.

Don't go! Daddy and I need you here with us. You bring so much joy into our lives. We will miss you so much our baby, sweet baby. Goodbye. So sad am I. I looked in his face. I saw the face of me. In a moment, I blinked. I looked at him again and I saw the face and body of his father.

She continued to cry. Her hands were shaking as if she was trying to shake out the pain of this great loss. A gentle melting of her hurt and pain. It was so visible on her face and body. She was on her knees now. Rocking back and forth, moaning in a low raspy voice she cried out the words,

Weeping Willow, are you weeping for me? What is a world without offspring? What is life without their innocent giggles, hugs, kisses, their many questions, their joy for life? All those cute noises they make, taking care of them. All their little scrapes and bruises. Why me?

Eyes big and round look towards the sky searching for an answer.

I did everything right. Didn't I? I do not know. Was it my fault? I ate right, I got enough sleep. We wanted him so. My husband and I. Why give our sweet baby to us then take him back? Why? I am a good person. I would have taken great care of him. It was not my fault, she said to herself over and over again.

Maybe I did not drink enough water. I just do not know.

Paula could not shake this feeling of responsibility.

The doctors at the hospital said, "We just don't know." It happens and there's no one to blame. I prayed so hard, 'Please do not take him,' when they told me he was leaving me. There was nothing more they could do. Everything in their expertise and everything in this universe had been done. It makes you feel so hopeless, so helpless. There's nothing you can do. Nothing. Oh! When it was time to say farewell to him. The nurses placed him in my arms for the first and last time. I sang one of the songs that was ours. "Hush little baby don't you cry mommy is going to..." I could not go on. It was too much. Is this for real? It had to be a dream. But it was not. The nurse took him away as tears ran down my face. I reached for him. She walked slowly towards the door with my baby. Then he was gone.

She moved closer to Weeping Willow. A hug was in order. Not saying a word. Just silence. She did not notice the traffic going by. Paula did not care that people stared, wondering, "What is she doing?" She was lost in a world of her own grief, not of her making, yet she continued with her story.

Days and nights afterward, the hurt in my heart and soul would not stop. My tears poured like raindrops. Shattering in a million tiny sparks as the tears fell towards the Earth and evaporated into the heavens and shines in the form of bright lights that twinkle like stars at me. Many nights my husband and I gazed up at the beautiful field of stars. Maybe one of them is his spirit communicating to us that he is alright. All my husband can do is comfort me as we hold and embrace each other. The memory was so clear in our minds. He rocked me ever so gently kissing my forehead. He was quiet in his own world of pain. I rested my head on his chest. I could feel and hear the beating of my husband's heart and feel the energy of our son. In the circle of his arms, I was comforted.

Weeping Willow didn't know what to make of this.

Can I do anything to comfort this person?

Weeping Willow started to move back and forth to create a cool breeze.

I will drop small leaves on her cheeks. It's the least I can do. She smiled. I let her know that this tree knows and understands. I feel your pain. Lady, you can survive this tragedy. It may not appear so now, but you will if you just hang in there. Give it some time. I know. This tree has witnessed miracles. Life is full of mysteries. Some wonderful, and some not so. They are all a part of the world we live in. We can choose to push forward. Live this wonderful gift called life. It's all we have, it's all we know. Look around you, it's beautiful.

She smiled to herself.

I get the message weeping willow.

Paula had an epiphany as she sat under this magnificent tree. Clear what direction her life will take. It is so simple to open your heart. One door closes another one opens.

Now I will get busy living this precious gift that was given to me, she announced to herself.

We each have our time on this Earth. It is not people who pick and choose who stays short or long term. It was taken out of our hands. Take time to grieve, do not be consumed by it. There is time for sorrow, there is a time for joy and celebration, she affirmed

She stood to her feet and reached out to touch the tree. Her hands rested there for a short time. She started to speak, clearer this time.

Baby, sweet baby, wherever you are in the universe, remember you were so wanted, so loved. In my womb, I carried you for nine months under my heart and I will feel your presence forever, my baby, sweet baby. You projected love to all the family. You gave me so much joy. You were a good baby. I will miss you always. Mommy will leave these flowers in honor of you and your short life. I will leave them at the base of this tree. You were here and made your presence known to daddy and me. We experienced your love. The memory of you will be in my heart forever. Farewell, my love on your journey back through the tunnel of life. Goodbye.

Her tears, now dried up, left white lines on her face imitating the paint on a canvas of lines on the freeway. She blew kisses in the air as she walked away.

I am sure I heard her say. "We will try again." She was smiling now. She got in her car. Turned the music on. Turned once to me. Started the car, this time, more slowly, easy. Then she was gone.

Story Six Poetry

"You"

People are running here and there.
What are they looking for?
They have forgotten the meaning of life.
It is a good woman, a good man.
The laughter of your little ones.
Seeing yourself over again in their eyes, the smiles on their faces.
The way they walk, the way they talk.
It is you.
Your love will endure through time.
Yes.
It is a man's world.
Life is no fun without your mate.
You have nothing.
Think about it.
There is more to life than just being here alone.
Baby her is my hand.
Let love be the vehicle of hope and peace for us.
Love will set you free.
Love will make you smile.
A smile like no other.

Love will bring rays of sunshine to your heart that will warm you all over.

Love will take away your sadness.

Love will help ease your pain.

It is about the power of an embrace.

The power of a touch.

It is about knowing where you belong.

Open your heart.

Let love find the way there.

When you really find it and you know it.

Do not let love slip away, slip away.

Do not be afraid.

Time is ticking and waits on no one.

Reach out.

I am here waiting.

Waiting for you.

Yes you.

STORY SEVEN

LITTLE SISTER

Hum, Hum. *What is going on? A group of young ladies are coming up the pathway. They are singing, skipping, and dancing. Swaying to the tune of their song.*

They stopped at the weeping willow tree.

We have got to get this together as a group. The song is from some of our life experiences.

The young ladies sang out loud, running around the trunk of the tree. They were so happy about the song they created together. They were in high school and spent a lot of time together. Best friends for life. Yeah. The young ladies were talking with such enthusiasm about how great they all had to be in the school's talent show.

We want to win. It will happen, this is our chance to show everyone what we can do, and that is sing.

"Exactly!" They said it at the same time. "We are amazing and awesome." They all burst out laughing. Hugging and high five to each other.

Very striking, tall, curvy, and so much personality in that girl. Lala was her name. She was the leader of the group. She started it. A take-charge kind of person. She is very sweet and oh so kind. Adored by everyone. Her voice was soft, that touched you like a beautiful melody when she spoke. Lala could dance, anytime. Her movements are very much perfect and beautiful. Lala could sing; the birds didn't have anything on her. Lala's family was very protective of her.

We all love them. Her mother was wonderful and always welcomed all of us. On her face was always an expression of being happy to see us. Lala's mother was always quoting words of wisdom to us. She had us sit in the den.

"I want you guys to stay healthy. Eat well to live, not live to eat. I know you will do what you want, but I am saying it because that is what I live by."

She always had vegetables, fruit, and water for us.
"Other foods in moderation. Enjoy yourselves. Make wise choices."

"Oh boy! Here she goes again," they thought to themselves.

"Do not take all that is offered to you. Sometimes in the shadows, evil lurks. Do not be afraid in life to take chances. Look out for each other. Remember to always be you. Now go out there in the world and sing. I will back you up if that is what you guys are seeking. Do not worry. When you guys venture out and things do not work out, remember, you can always come home. We will be here for you always. Love you."

GeeGee was very shy. She was on point though when she started to sing and perform. GeeGee was very analytical about everything. She had questions; what are you doing that for? Are you sure? She would break out in a big smile that could light up the room. After a little deliberation, she most often would say yes to any request. We were all so happy together. Never an argument that we could not work out between us.

Never a fight. GeeGee's family loved us. We were always welcome over to their home. GeeGee lived far from the school so it was easy to go and practice at the other two homes. They lived close to the school. The three of us planned to go to the same university and get our education in our various fields of study. Maybe help change the world in more ways than we could ever imagine. Music and education, we were going to be a double threat. Look out world here we come!

Jaw was tall and strong. Yet very kind and caring. Especially about us. She was our protector. She chose that title and lived up to it. We are family, all for one and one for all. If anyone messed with either of us, she was there like a streak of light. We never had trouble. Jaw knew how to talk us out of anything. She was a peacemaker. We were so glad we had her around. There were many sleepovers at Jaw's house. We would discuss our future and young men. But, the most important thing going on in our lives was music. We all agreed. We needed to practice, practice.
Jaw had a deep voice that resonated throughout the room. It made us laugh. Once we got started, it was hard to stop. All of us rolled on the bed or floor depending on where we were at that moment. We would clutch our stomachs and laugh so hard. Jaw's mother would come into the room. "What is going on! Are you all ok?" She would smile big. We also love her very much. "I see you young ladies are just having fun."

We were headed for stardom. Lala told us, "I have an idea. Let's rap the verses of the song now under this tree. That is what we came here to do."

They all started to move their hands, their feet, and body into a rhythm with the words of the song.

"Little sister, little sister
Grew up too fast, little sister trying to do good.
Doing the best, she could. Living in the hood.

Little sister, little sister has been called mama so long.
Did not know she was done wrong.
Too soon, too young, childhood gone.

Little sister, little sister memories ringing in my head, as we climb
Into our bunk beds. I hear you crying. Visions of you so cute in your
Sunday dress. Trying to impress, knowing everything is a mess.

Little sister, little sister jumping rope was her thang, so high trying to
reach the sky.
Trying hard not to cry, fighting back the tears for all her fears and lack of
years.
Little sister, little sister playing patty cake.
Oh! How her belly aches, oh how her belly aches.

Why do you take my innocence away? Cause I am not ready for this.
Please, someone, take it away. I looked in vain, with such dismay.
Because I can't do anything about your pain. I am little too.

Little sister, little sister out of the ashes like a burnt sweet potato.
Forever burnt with pain. Seen in your eyes brimming with tears.

Little sister, cry, let them flow to the floor.
Drain out all the years of pain and shame.
Dry your eyes and look towards the blue sky.

Beneath the burned skin, out of the ashes
is the sweet taste of the good life.
There is a brighter
Day. Dance little sister. You are special."

Wow! That is different. I like it. It was very entertaining and sad and emotional.

Weeping Willow shook, as he did when something touched him, just to see the young ladies so animated and really into their song. How beautiful all the young ladies look doing what they love best. The tree had not heard this music before.

I guess it is something new for the young people of today.

Leaves fell from the tree in honor of the young ladies and their song.

That's how much I like it.

Suddenly they stopped.

We are going to dedicate our song to all the little sisters of the world. We love you and we understand. We want them to know, they are not alone
.

The young ladies looked very serious.

What should we call ourselves, Weeping Willow? We cannot decide.

They all laughed.

"There are so many names to choose from. It should follow a certain theme. How about Strawberry, and the Hot Chocolates or Candy Canes and the Mellows, or Peaches and the Cobs. "

"Those names are making me hungry."

"Girl, me too."

They all continued to laugh.

We do not have to decide now. We will know when it is right. We all know it is a matter of time before we are off. Weeping Willow, we have been friends since grade school. Did we say that earlier? Anyway, we have wanted to sing since we held concerts at recess at school.

We heard it is a very difficult industry to venture into. We know, you either have it or you do not. People like you or they do not. But, having amazing talent helps. We are humble. We all grew singing in the church choir. The church is where we perfected our talent, our voices, and our singing styles. Our parents would let us sing at weddings and other small venues. It was so much fun. We didn't know how much of a focal point in lives it would play. We all also had training at school from voice and music classes. We are all naturals. Yeah, we have it. Wait and see.

You will hear our songs in the wind. The melody is going to blow right into your branches and down to your roots. You will know and remember us. We will travel all over the world and carry our message. Sounds awesome, right?

They patted and hugged the tree.

It is in our hearts and soul to do this. We know with courage and perseverance; we will do it!

They say it out loud, so their voices can be heard and carried by the wind.

All of us agreed that we are going to have an American theme in our outfits that we wear on stage to perform. U.S.A., Yeah. Each of us will have either all red, all white, and all blue. Represent where we came from. That is our plan. We also might mix the colors. There are many combinations we can alternate with these colors. We are so excited to have a clear direction about our dream for the future. We will make it happen. We can get it out there into the world.

"We will!" they shouted in unison. The young ladies all patted the tree.

We have to go now.

They rapped their song as they walked away., popping their fingers to their beat. The tree shook a little too.

It's a great song. Good luck.

The tree watched them fade in the distance, then they were gone.

STORY EIGHT

Don't Get In That Car!

Y oung and free. We were all, at one time in our lives, so innocent and trusting. Yes, the young think that nothing can happen to them. That the world is always kind. Many of us as children grew up in homes where religion was at the forefront of our everyday lives. Our house had the atmosphere of it always, thanks to our mother. We were sheltered for most of our youth and part of our early adult years. As children, we didn't know too much of the outside world beyond our house, our friend's house in our neighborhood, and our street that led to our school.

Oh! Around the corner and up the street was our church with a park across the street. We felt so safe and protected in our little world. It was like a small town in a bigger town. Life was so free and just plain fun. We thrived in it, my sister Sage and me, Spice. Close as two peas in a pod. We did everything together. You see one, you see the other. We played many games and had many adventures together.

This place is where we belong. We didn't think of ever leaving and going somewhere else. My parents taught all of us survival skills. What to do and what not to do. How far to go and how long to stay. Our father's rules were law in our house. He was the man and we all knew it without a shadow of a doubt. Our mother was sweet and gentle and spoke with a soft voice. She was the light disciplinarian and we, as children, listened and respected her in every way. She always said, "Listen to your father." If we did anything out of hand, she always said, "I am going to tell your father." We wanted our parents to be proud of us. We were children and *a little curious about some things, especially my sisters. We got into much trouble because of them.*

My father was like a king to us little ones. He was tall, dark, and handsome. He had a deep voice that resonated throughout the house. Whatever he said, we all knew he meant business. Dad was in the military. He was so proud and always wore his uniform with pride. He was such a striking figure in it. We did not know the suffering he had to endure and hide from us. Sometimes, when he talked about certain events, he got a look on his face. He was silent and thinking of the events of his past. Then after a few minutes, a big smile would return to his face and all was well in our world again. All we knew is that he was a soldier, and that was a very big deal to us. He would take us for walks to the store in his uniform. We felt so good and proud to say this is our dad.

After a tour of duty, walking through our door, he was a bright light to us children. Daddy was home and our happiness was out of this world. Dad would bring prizes from all over the world from the places he traveled. As he shared his stories with us, we were transferred back in time with him. It is great to play make-believe. Yeah! My father tempered everything with kindness and understanding. The apple does fall far from the tree. He was very wise and street smart. My father would gather us all around his large leather chair in the den, that was his place to talk to us. He told stories about himself, about growing up as a child, and how hard it was. His ups and downs and highs and lows. That's another story. Too much to tell now. Maybe I will write a book about him. Just maybe. Some say he was quite a man.

Ok, back to my story. As I stated before, my parents talked to us about survival.

"Remember what Daddy told you. Do not visit other places unless your mother or me... or as a matter of fact... Do not go anywhere until you let us know first. Once that door closes, Daddy won't be there to help you out. Understand?"

"Yes Daddy, we do."

"I do not want to frighten you, just try and keep you safe. It is a parent's responsibility to look after their children. Out of fear, we restrict you as you grow to adulthood. Children think we want to control them. No, my loves. It is losing you that we're afraid of. There are so many things that can happen. We know that we can keep you from many falls of life as you grow. We will try to do the best we can. The universe chose me as one of your guides to adulthood. Take a minute and look at the animals of the world and how they take care of their young. They protect and shelter them until the young are ready to fly or leave the nest. Should we as human beings do no less? Children are our gifts. They are precious in the sight of the universe's and my eyes. Do what I ask, children, and we all will be at peace. The law also goes for cars. Do not get into that car. Run home and tell me."

"Yes, Daddy, we hear you."

"Remember, do not let it get dark and the lights go out and you are not in the house."

"Yes, Daddy we hear you."

"People are good and kind but evil is out in the world, so listen to your parents. We want you all to just be aware if it does not feel right. Run!

Now let us watch tv until dinner is ready. We all know there is going to be a wonderful delicious home-cooked meal. Mom loves to show her cooking skills. She's the best."

Mother came out of the kitchen.

"I heard everything Daddy said and I agree."

Mom smiled and returned to the kitchen. The smell of the delicious dishes floated through the air. We were content and happy. Life is so good in our little corner of the world. I followed my mother into the kitchen to learn how to cook delicious tasty foods like her. Do not tell anyone.

The weeping willow tree was enjoying the beauty all around him. In the distance, coming up to him were two young ladies. One of them was talking in a very high pitch voice. Something had her going.

"Never, never will I get into another car or take a ride, unless I am driving that car, and I mean it" We should have taken the warnings of my parents. My father's words are ringing in my ears now. 'Don't get in that car!"'

One of the young ladies was telling her story to the other.

"Girl! Guess what happened to my sister and me."

"Tell me, tell me!"

She was excited now and they both sat down under the tree. The tree shook a little. He was excited to hear about their adventure.

My sister and I usually listen and follow the rules. Not this time. Small children grow up. Outside forces can push you to do something you know you shouldn't or you may just be a little curious. One beautiful day, my sister and I were coming home from school. It was a day like any other day., except that day we took a detour to the candy store. After leaving the store, a beautiful blue car pulled up beside us. The car was so bright, we could not see. We put our hands up over our eyes to be able to see. Two young men were in the car.

"Hi," one of them said. "Where are you two going? Want a ride?"

Immediately I said no.

"Oh, come on, we are harmless. We just want to show you how smooth this baby is. You won't regret it."

My sister and I looked at each other. I shook my head no but my sister took my hand.

"Let's go with them. They are young and cute."

Sage jumped in the back. I refused to let my sister go by herself, so I got in the front seat of the car. This would become one of the biggest mistakes of my young life, trusting our fellow man. We were soon to get a big lesson in life that I follow to this day: don't get in that car! Even if I know the person, I will not take a ride.

Anyway, we were riding through the neighborhood. The young man driving said something about being an expert in some kind of martial arts.

My sister did not believe him and replied, "No you are not! You can't do the high moves or chop anything."

Those comments set him off, but I think he was just waiting for a reason to do what he wanted to do all along.

Suddenly he changed and his voice was loud and angry. "I will show you what I can do!"

"Let us out of the car!" we screamed.

The young man did not say a word. He drove very fast towards the freeway, faster than before. The young man in the back seat did not say anything either. He looked terrified too. We do not know for sure. Boy, we are in it now! It was getting dark.

"What are we going to do? How are we going to get out of this car!" I was thinking hard to myself, and I am sure my Sage was also.

I was in the front seat and could not jump out. The young man driving smiled and was now looking directly at me.

"It has special locks. I control the locks," he said.

He had an expression on his face that sent the wrong vibe that made the hair stand on
the back of my neck. I could not jump out even if I wanted to. My sister was in the back seat and there was no way I could not leave her. Again, I could hear my father's voice, "If you go together, you come back together. That is the way it is. You look out for each other always."

The young man was driving so fast going upward in the hills somewhere. Looking out the window, I was trying to see a landmark. Wow! We could not see a thing.

"Oh God, where are we!"

I could feel my sister's eyes on the back of my head. She has a plan. I could hear in her voice that she was using everything within her to keep calm.

"I need to go to the bathroom," she said.

The driver turned his head towards the back seat like a snake.

"You better not go in my car! I don't know what I would do!"

He stopped the car with a jerk.

"Get out! Do it right by the door where I can see you. I am watching you. Do not try anything. I mean it."

As my sister was getting out of the car, our eyes met. This was our only chance. I got the message loud and clear.

With a sort of calm panic, I said, "I need to go also."
A lump was in my throat.

"Get out!" shouted the driver of the car.

Just as I was clear of the car door, my sister shouted, "Run!"

We both took off not knowing where we were going. We could not see anything, but we knew we had to get away from them. Desperate for safety, we looked for any place to hide. We jumped over the side of the road onto a steep slope. We realized fast that we were in trouble. We began sliding down this practically invisible mountain into the darkness

"Oh no!" I shouted.

We knew we had to be high up based on the uphill drive and sure enough, we were. We slid all the way down to the edge of the mountain and were hanging on the side of a cliff. My sister was holding on to my legs pulling me down. She had no choice. As we were sliding downward, my legs were the first thing she thought to grab onto.
We were so scared; you just don't know. We started to think about being eaten by bears and snakes.

"I am going to pull us up," I told her.

My hands dug into grass and dirt and moved slowly upward. I do not know how I found the strength to pull us up. All the training in physical education was paying off. I felt like a mountain climber trying to reach the top of the highest mountain peak. We made it to the top. Now what? We knew they were looking for us. In the far distance, we saw lights. We had to make a choice. We were crying hard now. Should we go with them or let the animals get to us? Can you believe, we were thinking of trying to talk and reason with the guys to take us out of the hills. The minds of innocent young ones. God bless the children.

Luckily, we did not have to make that choice. We were standing in the road shaking like frightened baby animals when a car pulled up. It was a young couple. They rolled their window down just a little to talk to us.

"What are you two doing up here?"

We were still crying so hard. We could not talk at first as we were so full of emotions. We had to tell them what happened to us and fast. We were so afraid that the guys would return any minute and we would have to fight for our lives. No way were we going to get in their car again. The couple listened to us tell our nighttime adventure which was still unfolding. They stared at us in disbelief, looked at each other, then back at us. We were still crying and looking in the direction of where the young men might show up any second. I have never been so afraid in my young life.

Bless them, they believed us. They could see how young we were. The young lady opened the back door and let us in. Thank you, thank you universe! We were so relieved. At the time, it hadn't occurred to us that we were getting in another car with people we did not know. Yet, there was something about them that made us feel at ease. We felt comfortable with them, no fear. It was something about the way they looked at us, the way they spoke to us with compassion in their voice. I am not sure how to explain it all. We just wanted to go home.

After we stopped crying, the young lady spoke again, "You guys are safe now. What are your names?"

"I am Spice and this is my sister Sage," I replied.

"We are taking the two of you home. Where shall we take you?"

We gave them the address of our older sister's place. The couple was gently chastising us all the way to our destination.

"Do you know how far up you were?"

"No," we replied softly.

"You know, we have never been in this area before. I guess it's better that you do not know how far up you were," the young lady said. "We are so glad we came along when we did."

I had no words to express my feelings of thank you.

"We were going to take the other route down," she continued, "but decided to take this route though we didn't really know why. The universe works in mysterious ways, I have heard. Maybe there is something to it." Her voice trailed off at the end as if she were speaking more to herself than to us.

Bless them. I hope life is good for the both of them. Our angles. They dropped us off at our sister's.

"Go inside. We will watch."
It was clear that they really cared about us. They made sure we were safe in our sister's house. My sister let us in. We turned and waved as the young couple drove away into the night. Then they were gone.

My sister was surprised to see us.

"Why are you guys out so late? Where have you been?"

We told her the story. She listened without any interruptions.

"Wow, that is quite a story. You are safe now. I will call our parents and let them know you guys are with me. Who were the people that dropped you off?"

My sister and I looked at each other.
"We do not know and we did not think to ask. They came to protect us. I do not know who sent the angels, but they came."

Grace was given to us that night. It could have turned out differently. We have lived to tell our story. My friends, I want you to feel that I pray for the two of you. Thinking of it today, it should have been reported to the police. I do not know why no one reported it. Maybe we felt the blame was on us for going with the guys. It is funny, my sister and I never spoke about it again. We just went on with our lives. It was a forgotten memory tucked away in the vault of our minds. We learned that night about good and evil. Good won that night. Maybe my mother's prayers were answered that night. "Take care of my children." She said she always put in a good word for us. Thank you, mom!

Girl! I'm telling you, walk, run, catch a bus, take any public transportation. Do it. Remember my father's words. It is so simple Don't get in that car!

The young lady started to cry.

I get emotional telling the story again. We never told my parents about it. We did not want Daddy to think of us any differently. He was so proud of us. He always said, "My girls are special." We were headed to adulthood and my father trusted us. We wanted that to stay the same. You understand? We needed that as children.

Both the young ladies stood to their feet. They touched the tree. "Thanks for listening," they say at the same time.

"Girl!" We should go and get home before dark."

 They walked briskly away from the tree and up the path from which they came. Then they were gone.

Weeping Willow tree was standing alone now. He was thinking about the story and the happy ending. The tree shook again a little, not sure why. The feeling went throughout his branches and leaves. The tree could hear, "Don't get in that car!"

Story Eight Poetry

"THE PURPOSE"

It is written in the stars.

It is carried in the wind.

It is whispered through the trees.

It is not their time.

They do not know yet their destiny is to give hope.

The universe has a purpose for them that is unfulfilled.

All the elements came together and said,

Let there be light.

And there it was.

The glow of your halo.

"Baby Let's Ride"

Wow man! look at those rims
look at that bumper on that frame.
She is built for speed.
Baby is built from headlights to backlights.
Just look at her. Man! she is pretty.
Baby so slick, Baby so smooth.
Baby new as a silver dollar.
Makes me want to holler.

"Come on baby, let's ride."
It is in the stars
I knew I had to have you.
Baby, you mine, So divine.
So fine, like a fine wine.
The aroma is so awesome.
Makes me feel out of control.
Man! she is something.
Come on, show your stuff.
Let us do whatever you want to do.
"Anything!"
"Come on baby, let's ride."
I open the door and slide in.

The touch is unreal.

I let the top down. The ride is divine.

She is built to go the distance

Baby, you and I will go places where others are afraid to go.

Speeds that defy gravity. My heart is beating so fast.

"Take my hand."

No longer on the ground, elevated to another place and time.

I want to race when I am with you.

"Come on baby, let's ride."

STORY NINE

THE MOTORCYCLIST

Sounds of a motor coming fast. Very loud. The motorcyclist bounced onto the curb.

Wait, wait!

The weeping willow tree was in a panic.

He's coming right up to me. Don't hit me! You might get hurt for sure. Your beautiful bike will get scratched.

The bike was in the colors of red, white, and blue. How American. The motorcyclist stopped his bike under the tree.

"Wow! You are something to see!" he said as he looked the tree up and down.

Spectacular! I need to rest for a while under your cool branches. If that's ok with you. I have traveled a long way on my bike to get to this point. Now, I long for home. That's where I am headed.

He placed his bike near him and smiled.

Well, my friend, we have a long trip ahead of us. I need to sleep. I know this tree doesn't care if I rest here.

Reasons unknown to him, he felt safe under this tree. The cyclist curled up very close to the trunk of the weeping willow tree, took his jacket off and rolled it up, placed his head on his jacket, and closed his eyes. He was out like a light switch that had been turned off. Weeping Willow kept watch over him.

Mister Mack married young, eager to experience this side of life. Mister Mack vowed to take care of his family who was always going to be number one in his life. He loved his young wife; she had been his high school sweetheart. She was right there with him through some of his problems in school. She was always there for him without question. She was gentle, kind, and patient. She was the one who held his head and comforted him when he needed it most. Early on in their relationship, he stated, "I am going to marry that girl. She is what I need in a mate for life."

Mister Mack was tall and handsome and had his share of female admirers. They did not have any effect on him. He had made his choice and that was that. Mister Mack and his lady love had a wonderful and blessed life. He was happy with his life and his wife, but one of his dreams was to ride his motorcycle across the great country of ours and take in all the beauty and spectacular sites. He needed to do it before he was not able to travel. It was the right time for his adventure, especially since his children were away at school. He was proud of their accomplishments at this junction in their lives. Mister Mack and his wife told them so often. He was so proud to have such wonderful people to contribute to this world. "They will do great work and change the lives of many." He was sure of it.

He was so excited to talk it over with his wife. They discussed it over their many years together.

Honey, the time is now for you to embark on this ride across the country and take the trip with some of your friends. Remember they had the same dream you did."

She was understanding that this was his dream. There were no objections from her. Tears welled in her eyes as she thought about how wonderful he had been to his family. Now it was time to give back. She was busy doing the work that she loved. It will fill her time while he is away. She had no desire to tag along with him on a motorcycle. She is happy at home and will be there when he returns.

All the guys were going to take off together and split at different points to follow their own itinerary and objections. Many of the guys stayed together through most of the trip. They felt a feeling of total freedom out on the road with the wind blowing against them. The feel of the bike under you, knowing you were in total control. Nothing to do but ride from place to place, town after town, city after city without a care in the world.

After visiting tourist attractions, many of the guys started to go in different directions. Mister Mack found himself alone and thinking of home. He had done what he set out to do. He felt good about his adventure and such a profound feeling of accomplishment. "Honey, I am on my way home to spend some time with the one I love." He was dreaming for sure.

Under Weeping Willow, he slept deeply. Mister Mack slept for a long time. Weeping Willow shook a little and covered him with leaves. This would keep other vehicles going by from seeing him. After hours of sleep, Mister Mack woke up. He was a little puzzled about all the leaves that covered him. He looked at the tree.

You did this? He got up and stretched.

Oh! That was good. Man! I really needed that rest to recharge. Now it is time to go.

He stood his bike upright. As he started to walk away, he paused and looked back at the tree.

I am going to tell my wife about this weeping willow tree.

He Smiled.

Thank you.

He jumped on his motorcycle, then he was gone.

STORY TEN

THE AIRPLANE

Weeping Willow is happy to have a bird family take residence in his tree. The birds are singing and chirping such beautiful songs. The birds are beautiful in all the colors of the rainbow. Blue and black ones, red and white ones, yellow and brown ones. As many color combinations as you can create. Some of the birds were as tiny as your thumb and how precious they all are.

Where do so many birds come from? Birds roam around constantly. Your car will get the residual of their travels. Mine has many times. The birds arrive in numbers appearing in the form of a dark gray cloud ascending into all of the trees, hiding from the sight of other animals who would love to feast on one of them.

Here's a little something about birds: they are warm-blooded. They are egg-laying vertebrates with feathers and wings. They are two-legged and small. Cute too. One of my favorite birds is the dove. It is the bird of peace and harmony.

All the birds have this instinct and will signal each other if needed. It is amazing how they look out for each other. You have probably heard the saying "birds of a feather flock together" meaning, people with the same characteristics and likes to stick together.

There are many things said about birds. I smile as I think about my parents saying many of them to us as children and even as adults. People say slang is ridiculous yet I believe they are words of wisdom. Think about what people are trying to convey to you. Their voices ring in my ear years later.

"It is better to have one bird in the hand rather than ten in the bush," meaning it is a sure thing. "Eat like a bird." I know you have heard this one, meaning do not eat too much. Take a little food.

Another that is well known, "birds and the bees;" adults trying to explain life to a child. Maybe someone should clarify this one for me, "bird brain," meaning stupid or nitwit. Birds are very smart even if they have a small brain.

Watch and listen to the birds and you will learn something valuable. You will always hear it. Birds have the gift of song. Hearing their sweet songs are calming to many of us.

I hear something else. Oh no! An airplane is coming towards me. I can hear the plane loud and clear. It's not too far off in the distance. The humming of the motor is so close. Trouble is surely headed this way.

In the colors of red, white, and blue a small plane with one person on board appears in the sky. The airplane is heavier than air. It is kept aloft by the aerodynamic forces of air upon its wings. Being licensed and qualified to operate the controls of an aircraft is the responsibility of all pilots. It is being driven forward by a screw propeller or jet propulsion. It was nearing the tree fast.

Zoom!

The pilot was struggling with some of the controls on the panel of the plane.

"It's here!" was all I could think.

Suddenly, the tree could feel the wind from the plane's propellers. Zoom! The tree spread out its branches as far as they would extend upward. A vision of an eagle soaring through the sky. wings stretched out.

I will catch you and break your fall.

Thinking of the family of birds that live there. Weeping Willow had to keep them safe.

Don't worry! This tree has many talents. I will do what is necessary to prevent anyone from getting hurt. You might get a scratch or two, but that is all. Be careful, pilot, you are too low! Go up if you can!

The tree shook in a panic.

All of me is shaking, my leaves are going everywhere.

Zoom. It grazed the tree a little.

Ouch. That hurt a bit.

In the nick of time, the pilot got control of the plane and pulled it up, up into the heavens.

Look at that plane. It is much like a bird. Soaring through the air, higher and higher. White clouds covered the plane and shielded it from the world below. No longer could I see him. I could hear only a little engine far in the distance. Then he was gone.

STORY

ELEVEN

CAN I

Hello, hello?

It was a voice the tree had heard before, soft and sweet. She sounded excited as if she were looking for someone.

Remember me?

She waved at the weeping willow tree as she neared it coming up the path.

It's me, Shay. Don't you remember? As a child, I lived here. A few miles away. I am one of the children who played here under your branches. Well, here I am, back to see you, as an adult. Life has given me many ups and downs. Weeping Willow, I have been tested by many trials and tribulations over the years. Yes, the years have passed by so quickly. There have been many storms to be brave through.

The tree perked up and shook a little.

Oh, I remember her. The playful one. She is back to visit with me. How wonderful.

Shay started to speak again. She looked up at the tree with tears in her eyes and voice. At any moment they were going to flow.

Weeping Willow, life was not served to me on a silver platter, as a manner of speaking. I have worked hard, long, long hours day and night. I enjoyed work.

It was clear that Shay always tried to do the right thing.

People want so much from you. I am only one person. It didn't matter what I did. It was never enough, in some cases. People can twist events and occurrences Things are not always what they appear to be. Everything must go their way, even if they are not right. It's life. Some people can get away with so much and people just turn their heads. People believe everything they say. That's how it is, so accept it and move on.

I tried to set things right. No one wanted to hear the truth. There is nothing you can do about it. On occasion, you have too much on your plate and the box is closing in on you from all sides. It's not clear to you what has taken place. You pick up the pieces of your life and move on. You are a strong woman so you go for it and just do it. Maybe someday they will think back on it and understand. They will listen with an open heart. They will know what it was like to walk in your shoes. The pain and the hurt you have endured. The lies you had to fan off.

I kept climbing, not being distracted by the many obstacles that were thrown directly in my path. Many days you are so tired all you want to do is lay in your bed and cover your head and sleep. Maybe when you wake, things will be different. All the stuff from the past will dissipate in a big bubble and float into outer space. Gone and forgotten.

Anyway, I am here to share my song with you. It is called "Can I." "Can I" has been deep down in my soul for a long time. Maybe too long. The song just erupted out of me one day. The words poured out from my full heart. Weeping Willow, you just don't know how wonderful it is to have a place to come to. Where you can find peace and quiet. Where you can pour out your troubled heart and sort out life. Someone to just listen. No judgment of any kind. Here I am again to laugh, dance, and be happy, as I was when I was a child here. So, Weeping Willow, I bring my song to you.

Shay started to sing and dance around the tree as she had years before. This time, there were many tears as she sang her song.

"Forgive me please?" Weeping Willow thought. "Is she asking me or someone else? I do not know, hmmm."

The music from her song started to resonate through the branches of the tree. Weeping Willow was so moved that some of his leaves fell to the Earth. As a few of the leaves fell, there was a breeze that picked the leaves up and blew them up, up to be carried into many yards, valleys low and high, and on hilltops.

Awesome.

Can I?
Praying, praying to you my lord, asking.
Can I lay my burdens at your feet?
Can I, can I?

This world is so full of hate. We wait for peace.
Year after year, it stays the same. It is a shame.

Who is the blame?
It is hard to deal with all this strife.
Many say stay strong. It will get better.

Lord, Lord can I lay my burdens at your feet.
They are killing our children in the street.
I carry too many sacks on my back.

I hunger for relief. My heart hurts. My stomach is hollow.
It is hard to beg for another dollar. I feel like I want to holler.

Can I, can I?
It feels like I am going under. Barely can I lift my head up one more time.
Please lord, let me lay my burdens at your feet?

Can I, can I?
A new direction is where I am going. A new light for someone.
A new attitude of hope and healing for our world and me.
Maybe I can make a difference. With your help
I will press on.

Suddenly Shay stopped singing. She came over and sat under the tree. She spoke again, very softly as she leaned her head against it.

The other day, I picked up the phone and called my brother. We have been distant for years. When he answered the phone and said "hello," all the old wounds fell away. It was as if we never had a disagreement. Now, I do not know what it was all about. I am quite sure in the big scheme of life it was nothing. Now, it was not worth remembering.

"How could we have let so much time slip away?" we both wondered. *I do not know, but I suggested we get together soon, for sure.*

Shay touched the tree, to transfer her feeling of happiness to the tree. *I can barely wait to see him. Family is very important. I will treasure my family from now on, with appreciation and understanding as my guide.*

The tree let leaves fall on her gently. She put her hands up and caught a few in her hands.

"This is what I remember," Shay said as she sat down again.

Her mind raced back in time to a past full of family. They were all close at that time and Shay and her brother had a special bond. They always took care of each other. They had many friends. Their friends made her feel so special. She smiled thinking about how her brother looked up to her. He made her feel beautiful and loved throughout their life.

Many galas with their friends would astound you at the splendor of such occasions. The group of them dressed to dazzle from head to toe. It was awesome! Walking into any affair, heads would turn. So many handsome young men and beautiful young ladies.

We were all so striking. Brother looked good though. He always had a friendly smile. I am showing a little favor if that is ok with you.

Shay blushed.

We were ready to party. We should have been professional dancers. Dancing was in our blood. Our parents were expert dancers in their youth.

Now here we are, chips off their blocks, taking over the dance floor. We danced the shoes off other dancers at all the hot spots. We were at the top of buildings, in underground clubs, parties in the streets and parties at the beaches. The guys protected all the ladies, we felt so safe anywhere. Our life was a blast.

The lady smiled again as her memory wandered back even farther. It was just the two of them against the world. They shared everything. It was a glorious time. Life was so good. They had quiet times, and many discussions about what the future held for them. They both also had a passion for helping others. Shay's brother had a kind heart and was generous to all who knew him.

We talked about getting married and having children. He said, "I bet I will be the first to get married." "Yeah." We had visions of being the best parent ever. "Just like Dad and Mom."

Shay was silent, looking out beyond the tree and his world. Back out there from which she came.

Oh! I almost forgot. Another incident that perplexed me. Though it is not a burden to me. Maybe someone will stop and think about the gift being given to them. On a visit to a professional facility to take care of business, I was feeling wonderful. I anticipated a warm greeting from the person that was there to meet me. I was smiling, happy to be feeling so good.

"Hello," I said. The reply was startling.

"I am sick and tired of people coming in here with all those different smells and perfumes on them. I have allergies and I am sick of it."

I looked around to see who was there with me. Was she talking to me? I didn't say anything, I just stood there in shock at this display of anger. Silence is all that can be done in certain incidents.

"Use professionalism, please. Talk to your management about the conditions you mentioned," I suggested.

"I am in this small space all day. It is hard to breathe," she complained.

I felt sympathy for her. She was in her own little world of agony.

I spoke to her calmly, "You chose this job. Do not take feelings of anger on the visitors. Having a bad day. Take off. My spirit of happiness was crushed in those few moments. Think about it. That's not how I would like to be treated. Collect yourself and do a great job."

"Ok," she replied humbly.

"All is forgiven. I am looking for this department."

Shay was lost in the memory for a few moments longer. Slowly she came back to reality and knew it was almost time to go.

"Just a little longer with the tree," she thought to herself

Shay took the piece of paper that her song was written on, folded it, and placed it in a little hole she dug at the foot of the tree.

What is she doing? Hmmm.

The tree was curious. Shay stood up slowly.

The song is yours now. I feel so strong and free after my visit with you. Thank you for all the memories, my friend.

She touched the tree once more.

I am ready to face whatever life brings my way now.

She walked to the street and turned right. The tree could see her in the distance for a long time. Then she was gone.

****

Weeping Willow was getting ready for the night when the stars and the moon came out to keep him entertained with their light show.

How beautiful when the sun goes down. Someone is coming. It is Shay rushing back to me! She is back so soon. What is going on?

Shay started to talk so fast.

I have another memory to leave here at the foot of this tree. There is no need for me to carry it around. Last week, I dropped my vehicle off at the car shop. I have heard so many stories about women being taken advantage of and it is true.

I never thought it would happen to me, but it did. My car had some tightness. The car was not giving me a smooth ride as it usually did. It's usually as smooth as a yacht on a calm sea. Driving to the car shop, I was laughing and feeling so good about life and getting my car repaired.

"I am going to take care of you. Soon you will be gliding as smooth as a professional ice skater on the arena floor. Yeah!" I patted the dash of the car. This was a new shop for me and was recommended by my friend, Buddy. On arrival at the shop, a man greeted me.

"What can I do for you today?" he asked.

"Inspect my car to see what is going on with it. My name is Shay. I am here on the suggestion of my friend Buddy."

"Oh yeah! I know him."

"My baby is not running up to par."

"We will need to keep the car overnight, possibly a few days. I will call you to keep you updated. Do you need a ride?"

Just as he finished his question, my ride pulled up. Honk! honk!

"There is my ride. Thank you. Bye!"

On arrival home, I realized I had not gotten a receipt. Oh well, he was recommended. He must be ok, or so I assumed. I did not think more about it that day. A few days passed and there was no call from the shop. So, I decided to call the car shop to check on their progress. The guy I met that day answered the phone.

"Sorry about not calling you, we have been extremely busy," he explained. "The car needs a few parts. Luckily, it will not cost much. It will be ready tomorrow."

"Okay thank you." I was so happy. I decided I would call Buddy and thank him.

A few more days passed. I was being patient with this car shop. I had no choice; they had my car. I was waiting for the call stating that the car was ready.

Weeping Willow, I was feeling good. I had to work over extra days to make sure I had enough money to pay for the repairs. I love my job, so I did not mind. I finally decided to go pick up the car. It ended up costing much more than expected.

"You said there was not much wrong with the car." I lamented. Instead of making a big scene, I went ahead and paid. I was happy to get it out of there and test drive it on the way home.

Two miles from the car shop my car started to shake.

"What?"

I pulled over.

"Okay, Shay, collect yourself. Breathe," is what I always tell myself when I am in a pickle.

I turned around and took the car back to the shop, shaking all the way. My car would not stop shaking. They looked under the hood of the car.

"We will check out the car. It will be ready tomorrow."

Now you know I was steaming. I went home before I said something that I would regret later. The guy from the car shop called the next day like he said he would.

"Your car is ready. It'll cost a little more to fix it. Your car needed another part."

"What!"

I could not believe it. I gave the car shop enough money. I had to shell out more money than the car shop originally quoted me. Much more. I went to pick it up as soon as possible. *I test drove the car and felt the smooth ride and quiet of the car.*

Weeping Willow, do you know what lessons I learned that day? I learned a few valuable ones. That you are never too mature to learn.

Shay smiled to herself then she broke out in laughter.

I was madder than a wet hen about the incident at the car shop. It really upset me. They really thought that they could get away with overcharging me. I am not worried about it because there is a higher power watching. I am at peace with it now. I let it go.

Shay stood and raised her hands.

I have to go! How time flies by. I have stayed longer than planned. My beautiful car is out in the distance.

Shay touched the tree.

This has been a full day. Thank you for listening. I needed to vent and now it was over.

Shay ran to her car, got in, sat for a minute, and started the car. Then she was gone.

STORY TWELVE

THE COMPUTER

Weeping Willow tree does not recognize the woman walking up the path to him. She is well dressed in a silk dress with a matching coat. It's a glorious day to have a visitor in such glamour. She reached out to touch the tree with a warm greeting.

Hello, my friend. I know you have missed me. Right?

She smiled a big smile so happy to be here with a Weeping Willow.

I have not been to see you for a few months. Mrs. V. is a working woman now. I have longed for my days of just sitting under your cool branches and telling you about my life as a wife and mother. I have only good things to say about that area of my life. It's all good. Everything, as a matter of fact, is great.

I am going to tell you what occurred to me on the new job; I know that we are not alone. If you believe, the Universe's powers will help you. We are in the presence of a higher power. Call it what you will, but I experience its power. Listen to my story as I share it with you, Weeping Willow.

In this wonderful modern age of great technology, everything is at the touch of a finger. For many of us, it can be a little overpowering and just as frightening. Mrs. V. had been a stay at home mom. Life was good at home. Her children were now in school. After being at home for years, she was thinking about returning to work. The thought of this new world was fascinating to her. What would she do out in this new world? What can she do? She had run her home with great efficiency and comfort for the family. The children were wonderful. They were easy to care for. Good attitudes, like their parents. She is giving her parents some of the credit for this outcome. They did the best they could in all matters. They were always fair and weighed everything. Their love surrounded their children as a warm coat did.

All of us felt so wanted and protected. What a wonderful feeling to have someone watch over you and keep you safe. I have been told that the apple doesn't fall too far from the tree. We are great as parents. We emulated our parents combined with our own ideas that work together well. Now here I am taking that flight again out of the nest. It is such an exciting journey that I am about to embark upon. Job searching was a little intimidating. Friends advised me on which sites to look at.

They were so happy for Mrs. V. They had wanted her to join them for a long time. Here she is about to join them in this wonderful world of discovery. They were going to go out to lunch in one of the finest restaurants. It was one of their great pleasures they shared with her. Meet after work and have more fun at some of the trendy spots that the city has to offer. Mrs. V.'s friends couldn't understand the reason for her fears. She had made her mind up; she was going to start out slow. Get her feet wet just a little. Nothing too serious. She was thinking very hard about it.

An easy schedule would be great. She was going to take different assignments until she found her dream job. She was so nervous as she got ready to go that morning for her first interview. Mrs. V. showed up very early and waited with much anticipation. She had been apprehensive for nothing. She was hired that very day. Mrs. V. was happy and nervous at the same time.

"Wow! I still have that winning personality," she smiled to herself. A memory that only she understood.

This is great news for her husband who was not sure she was serious. Mrs. V. could not wait to tell him. She raced home as fast as she could and told him the good news with such fervor and excitement. He was so happy for her. He took her in his arms and swirled her around with joy.

"Honey, I am so proud of you. How impressive!"

Their children were jumping for joy also. "Mom you did it!" This was the first time the children would have to share their mom with anyone other than family. Oh, how this change is going to affect their everyday lives. Only time would tell. Mrs. V. reassured the children that everything would be the same. She would be at home when they arrived from school.

"Now, let's eat dinner. We are all going to bed early. Mom is a working woman and she is getting up very early."

The children smiled and agreed with her. "Mom, you don't want to be late on your first day."

"You guys are so right, now to bed."

Mrs. V. always wanted a husband and children, a family to call her own. Many conversations were had with her friends growing up about what was needed to be happy in life. Most of them wanted a family. Not all, but most. Mrs. V. knew the first time she and her husband met what the outcome was going to be. They just knew. It was written in the stars and so shall it be done. He was everything she wanted in a man. They were ready for love and a family together.

They had an adequate income to support themselves and a family. Mrs. V. worked hard and saved her money. They both were very blessed to find each other. You can't mess with destiny. *We both had gone to Universities and had a great time. We met many suitors. None of them was the right one. We both traveled to many destinations just to come home and find true love, the one we had been searching for. It was true love, real love.*

He stated, "I will take care of you and do all that is humanly possible for my family." She got lucky with her husband. He loved them so much. "Yes, it was love, truth, and loyalty that I gave to you. In return, you gave me awesome royalties, our children. Thank you."

Ms. V. got up early for work that first day. She wanted to get there early to meet everyone and find out her routine and what would be required of her. She tried to brave this new world with confidence. At that moment, fear was trying to creep in. Everyone was so nice and friendly. They welcomed her with smiles on their faces. She felt a little at ease, but still a little nervous. Mrs. V. loved to do different tasks.

I am excellent at whatever I do. Just ask anyone who I am acquainted with.

Not too long after arriving, the supervisor came over.

"We have a project for you to work on. We need it today, if possible. You will be required to use a computer."

"Oh, wow. My first day. I have not been on a computer in a long time."

Mrs. V. was not sure of herself where the computer was concerned. She was terrified of not doing a good job on her first day. They showed her to the computer.

They explained the project to me. I looked at the computer and I froze. I couldn't think. I knew they were depending on me. I didn't want to say I couldn't do it. They had faith in me to help with this project.

She sat there consumed with all the fears she had carried about computers. She turned the computer on.

Now what? I almost started to cry. In my desperation, I asked for help. I heard myself say the words, "God, please help me."

Weeping Willow, I am not sure what happened. All I know is assistance was given to me from somewhere. My imagination, or the computer bank in my mind, tapped open to reveal what was imprinted there from a time before. Maybe a world beyond what we know. Or possibly a duplicate of me in another time and space watching me, moving with me, living my life as I live her life as one. Everything started to flood in me about the computer program.

I tell you as I live and breathe, I had never worked on this program before. It's hard for me to believe and understand what had transpired in that office. Something took over me. A light went off. It was me but not me. I was able to work on the computer and finish the project. I wanted to jump for joy and say I did it. Instead, I just sat there facing the computer with tears running down my face.

How did it happen? I don't know. In my time of need, someone or something was there to help me. I stared at the computer for the longest time. Are you there on the other side reaching out to help? I didn't know what to think. I have the finished project to prove it.

Who you are, wherever you are, thank you. I got much praise that day for finishing the project in such a short time. "We are so happy to have you join our team. You did a great job," they told me.

Weeping Willow, I had to come and share my story with you. I believe life is so full of mysteries and unexplained events. I knew you would understand and believe it happened to me. You are always here to help me sort out the confusion when I am not sure. There are many scenarios we might assume. How do I explain it?

Maybe in the small recesses of our brains, there is a link to a small planet triggered by the right situation where you can do miraculous things. People have been known to do extraordinary things. Move objects with their mind or one person moving heavy objects in an emergency. How do we explain it? Scientists are doing many studies on the brain. Maybe someday we all will have answers.

Mrs. V. stood on her feet and touched the tree.

I could not tell anyone about it. Now I am telling the world through you. The world will know about it now and I will not be afraid. It's time for me to leave. The children will be waiting for me at home. See you another time, my friend.

Mrs. V. walked hurriedly towards the streets. She turned right where she had parked her car. She got in. Then she was gone.

STORY

THIRTEEN

THE VAN

S low, so slowly as if surveying the area, a large van pulled up and stopped. A lady embarked off the van smiling.

Hooray! We are here! What a terrific place!

She was wearing red, white, and blue. She walked around to the other side of the van, opened the side door of the van, and lowered the step.

"Ok, everyone, let's picnic under this great tree. It's magnificent. Is this ok with all of you guys?"

"Yes," was their reply in unison.

The other staff person, a male, jumped down off the van without using the step.

"You are feeling athletic and robust this morning," the woman pointed out.

He laughed, "Yea! I will assist anyone who needs it and get all the students off the van."

He was so nice to all the students.

"You guys are awesome!" he would remind them.

All the students were getting off the van with such happy faces and thanked the man as they went, "Thank you, thank you!"

They pointed at the weeping willow. Wow! How pretty.

I am so happy to see all these young people here to see me today. Sweet!

Weeping Willow felt so good.

Happiness for me is to have visitors. They talk to me and fill my world with joy. Everyone was so happy. Some of them use a metal device for walking. One is in a wheelchair. One carries a cane. Some walk with a limp.

They all laugh as they move towards Weeping Willow with excitement. Last but least, the final student to get off the van was a young woman. She jumped down off the van.

"I am Gaia, guardian of the Universe. My mission is justice and peace for all."

Gaia whipped her long black hair around with a snap. It was as black as the darkest piece of coal. It can wrap you in a vice grip very tight.

To do good is what I am here for.

"Gaia be careful!" said both staff members at the same time as they watched Gaia's careless descent from the van.

Gaia laughed as she threw her head back. Gaia is sweet and delicate. They all admired her very much for her strong spirit.

"Yes, Gaia, you are unique," the female staff said as she smiled. It was true, Gaia was so amazing.

How patient and caring the staff woman was with all the students. She spoke softly to all of them.

I feel something good about this lady. She seems like an extraordinary person. All the students wanted to be around her and hug her at the same time. I can hear her laughter as it went through me like a sweet song.

The male staffer was watching and he chimed in, "They really love you."

"Yes. It radiates from them." They both laughed.

"They love you also," the woman said to the man. I know you feel it and see it in their actions towards you."

"Thank You, your kindness is appreciated, and you're right, I think they do love me," was his reply.

He was rubbing his cheek, playing the shy one. He was funny like that. He was shy about compliments and praise. He loved his job teaching very much. He especially loved being with his students. Teaching is what he has wanted all his life. Giving back to others. He is one of a kind, who really cares about his students. A truly exceptional person.

The staff woman thought to herself for a few moments, it is such a pleasure to work with him. We work so well together. Such understanding and great cooperation on both our parts to make it work. I like him like a brother and friend. Nothing more. People think there is more because we are so close. You meet someone and right away you know that there is a connection. It feels as if you met before and you will be great friends."

Gaia touched the last step, and as she finished her dramatic exit, she almost tripped. The woman's arm caught her fall.

Wow, that was close! You were here and I didn't fall. Thank you. Gaia was grateful.

Anyone one can trip, it's ok.

The female staff member knew what she was trained to do; make sure students are safe.
"I have taken care of many incidents but I love my job," she whispered aloud to herself and the tree as if she were letting him in on something the tree thought was important. The other students were quiet for a few minutes. The smallest incident could upset them.

"Everything is alright, staff is here for you. If for any reason we did not assist you guys, as we are trained or we are incapacitated in some way, we'd find a way to keep you safe. We will always take care of you guys in any way that is in our powers to handle." Female staff turned to male staff, "Should we call the school?"

"No, thank goodness."

If anything occurs, all staff are instructed to call the school. But all was well here. The weeping willow tree was watching. He shook a little as he felt something move him. His leaves fell gently on them. All the students raised their hands to catch some of the falling leaves with such joy and delight. Their world was happy. Their attention was on the falling leaves. Weeping Willow was so happy to bring such joy to them.

The staffers began praising the students, "You guys are just wonderful." "You are handling yourself just great. We are so proud of you all."

The man raised his hand up in the air to give a toast with a can of soda.

"Cheers!" he shouted

The woman looked directly at him, "You know you are not to drink that stuff."

"You know I love my cola. Much too much," he smiled.

"Oh, I do!"

Everyone broke out in laughter as the Man downed his Cola.

Hand me another one? he said heartily. He couldn't control his smile. It was very wide from ear to ear. "So good, so good!" he exclaimed. "But enough about me. Let us have lunch."

It's almost past our lunchtime and they were all so hungry. Everyone had their lunches out and ready to chow down. They eat as if in a hurry. Come on you guys. Slow down, the woman said gently.

Music was playing on the radio as everyone sang along. The students were so into music. They loved it. Everyone was having such a great time. One of the students with a big smile on her face shouted with glee.

"I can sing, I can sing."

"Ok, let us hear it," the man encouraged.

She began to sing.

Yes, somebody loves me
because my teacher told me so.
And that makes me feel so good.

"Yay!" Each of the students put their hands together to give a loud round of applause.

Wow! That was beautiful, you sound so professional. We knew you could sing, but that was awesome. We all want to sing that," the woman said, genuinely surprised.

The entire group started to sing that song.

"You guys sound so awesome also," she complimented.

The staff joined in. Everyone's enthusiasm was in the air and in their hearts.

Now that was creative, fun, and just plain amazing. Thank you for sharing. Give me five!

All of the students raised their hands eager to have them touched with such congratulations for each other. It was a beautiful sight to see, it warmed everyone's hearts. After they all finished lunch, almost at the same time, the students all wanted to stay longer at the park to tell their stories about themselves.

What is this, show and tell talent? the man chuckled. Ok, ok, we have time, we don't have to leave yet. he said. He looked to the woman, you take over, I will lean back and watch.

Ok. You guys can take turns. Does that sound like a good idea? She pointed to one of the students. "You first, Sheba."

I am a beautiful princess who is waiting for her prince charming.

Everyone laughed.

He is going to take you to a grand castle to live happily ever after. Oh! And give you extravagant gifts, the woman assured her.

Sheba smiled," Exactly!"

Next came Sal. "My turn, my turn" he piped in. I can dance faster than anyone here.

We all believe you, but don't you think you should take your time? Don't move too fast, the woman warned.

The man chimed in, "Agreed, Mr. Sal. You know what can happen. Let's be safe, correct?"

Sal smiled at the staff, "Ok, Cool. I will wait until I get on stage."

"Correct."

The staff lady sat with the students, thinking this would be their last outing with her. It was time for her to go. Duty calls somewhere else. It was a difficult decision, but she had to make life choices. Tears rolled down her cheeks hitting the Earth like small diamonds, burying her pain beneath the weeping willow tree. She will miss her students tremendously.

What is the matter? The man was concerned.
He looked over at the woman and noticed her tears. Why are you crying? Are you touched by the students singing? he asked gently.

"Yes," she whispered, waving her hand.

She did not want her students to see her crying. This was a happy time and that's how she wanted all her students to remember the good times they had with her. She started to reminisce about her life. The life of her students and how their lives intertwined. How destiny brought her to them. She wanted to do something in her life that would make a difference in someone's life who needed her.

She sat quietly and thought to herself. Life is beautiful. Waking up every morning with a song in my heart eager to face whatever life has to offer with much enthusiasm. Life is a gift. We are here to enjoy and live our lives. Move, play, overcome obstacles, and win victories throughout life. There are many among us who need a little help to achieve small everyday victories. Adults and children with developmental disabilities. Our goal is to help them live fully independent lives to the best of their potential. They need to feel secure, loved, and like they belong. Helping my students to do as much as they can with dignity and respect is a top priority. They are in a world that is not of their making. Yet they smile. My life is richer and fuller. I appreciate every day working with them. They will warm anyone's heart and spirits will soar. They make you feel very important. You are doing something that is making this a better world for someone. They are thankful for everything you do. You know it's for real when they say. "Glad to see you." and you see that the smiles are from their hearts. A journey of a thousand miles begins with a single step. That's what I did. My students have taught me so much about life and living. Most people have no problem that they can't overcome. Everything in my life is viewed from a different perspective. As our life's journey takes us here and there, we should seek out new avenues. Give. Pay it forward. Reach out. They are waiting."

She told no one that she was leaving. Not even the man. Not yet anyway. She did not want to cause her students or anyone else any pain about her leaving. In life, sometimes life's pressures and responsibilities take control. Life goes on.

She got up, wiped her tears, and faced the students. "Let's continue," she said.

West, another student stood up and shouted to everyone with much excitement, I am going to be a preacher one day. Isn't that great? I am so happy. I hope to teach the world to sing happy songs. I want to spread peace and love all over the world. Be an advocate for all the people."

"Yes, we are so happy for you! the entire group said in unison. We will all come to your church."

West smiled big, "I can't wait to see you all there."

West stood and took a bow. He was brimming with personality and charm. He is sure to make wonderful changes in the world. They all knew it. It was Pete's turn. He stood and started to sing beautifully.

Weeping Willow tree shook a little with emotion as Pete's voice rang out touching the tree's roots, stimulating the tree's leaves to fall gently on Pete. Pete reached for the woman when the song was over.

"I love you," Pete told her.

It was a precious magical moment. She smiled at him.

"Thank you, Pete. I think you are so inspiring to all. It's very nice. Pete, you have so much talent. We will see you at the opera house. We all know it will happen one day. Yeah."

The woman fought back tears, yet she managed to keep them at bay as she introduced the next student.

"Meri has something to show us. Wow! Look at this! I love it, I love it!"

Meri was overly excited as she held her toy proudly in front of her. "My teddy bear purse!" she smiled as she showed it off. She held it in the air for all to see.

Meri was so elegant in her movements and description of her items which is just like her. She had so many dazzling things that she loved to show and tell. Meri was such a delightful and beautiful person.

"I am going to be a fashion designer," she announced to everyone.

"You will, I am sure of it," The woman said with a big smile on her face. She had much affection for Meri. She was so helpful in so many ways, whenever you need her.

Bobby stood with much anticipation. Bobby was being silly and trying to sing.

"Bobby you can't sing!" They all laughed together. "Let's sing again."

It was beautiful how the students understood each other.

"You are the best. We all like your enthusiasm, Bobby. Trying to do your best and it is well received," the woman encouraged.

He bowed, "See you on stage!"

"The students bring so much fun to the table," the woman thought aloud. "Right?" She directed her question to the man.

"Yes. It has been such a pleasure being with the students on this picnic today. I am happy."

Everyone got to their feet and started to dance and dance. They went in circles around the tree. They raised their hands in delight and laughed as they danced. As the picnic lunch progressed and they danced, dragonflies appeared around the area in beautiful sparkling colors of pink, blue, green, gray, black, and brown, many colors of the Earth. They came close to the students and man and woman, but not too close. All the students raised their hands trying to get one of the dragonflies to land on their hands. The dragonflies twirled and danced in the air dazzling all who saw their awesome display. One of the dragonflies came very close to the staff lady. Uh-huh! If she wanted to, she could have reached out and touched it, but she didn't. The dragonflies continued to fly around near the lady. She smiled, very much intrigued by this attention from them.

She spoke out loud, "I guess the dragonflies think I am a tree. Do you think they will lie on me?"

Everyone laughed with excitement. "They will if you stand there longer!" someone shouted.

The woman felt good that she could make everyone so happy, including the dragonflies. Weeping Willow wanted to get in on the fun. The tree shook a little making a cool breeze that made everyone comment on how nice that felt.

"What wonders of nature! Some are small, some are large, but oh, to the eyes that see them. Unbelievable! Breathtaking! We witnessed it today. It made all of us feel special and a little closer to nature. We shall keep it tucked away in a small corner of our hearts, and just remember," the woman thought to herself.

The tree was still blowing, feeling so happy about today. His thoughts were interrupted by the staff's voices.
"Time to go! We do not want to go yet either. But we all know we should be back at school before departure time."

I don't want you guys to go yet. I was having such fun, and it's still early. I kept you guys cool on this hot summer day. It can't be because you are hot.

The students gave a big sigh and stretched. The group smiled at the tree.

"You are enchanting, Weeping Willow. You have made our day more beautiful. We all will carry the happy memories with us." The woman felt a tug at her heart. "The picnic under this magnificent tree will carry us through another day. How grateful we are."

The group cleaned up everything. It was as if they had never been there. Not a piece of paper, a bottle, a can, or food.

This is incredible. Very impressive, you guys.

Each one of the students hugged the tree as they were leaving. Some placed their cheek next to the trunk of the tree, stood for a moment, and said thank you. Memories of another time came racing back to the tree. The tree shook a little and his branches started to droop.

Stop it! I am getting ahead of myself.

The tree chastised himself and was brought back into reality by the sound of the van's motor. All the students proceeded to load up in the van and waved at the tree as they settled in. The tree could hear the staff calling out their names. All here! Great! They drove off in their red, white, and blue van. The sign on the back-license plate of the bus read "Handicap."

Hm-mmm.

The tree's branches shook as he watched them drive off. Then they were gone.

Story Thirteen Poetry

"My Purpose Was You"

Before you leave this planet.

Someone touched them with a gentle hand.

Someone smiled at them from within.

Someone said kind words to them.

Someone did take care of you.

Someone did watch over you.

Someone gave them water when they were thirsty.

Someone gave them food when hungry.

Someone held their hand in the park as we walked together.

Someone made them smile.

Someone listened to their request.

Really listen and ask the question.

What do you desire?

I will assist you.

I am here for you, that was my purpose.

"GOODBYES"

People come and they go.

In and out. Our paths cross.

Our lives are different.

Yet the same in many ways.

So soon you are gone.

My heart touched for a moment, a minute in time.

Now, missing you my friend most of all.

I will miss your kindness.

The gentle touch of your hands.

The sweet sound of your voice

The circle of your hugs.

People come and go.

So quickly, so quiet their goodbye.

"CELEBRATE YOU"

Be happy, love yourself

you are worthy. Be peaceful, be joyful.

Let your heart and soul sing

Birds come out to sing for you.

Smile from within.

Let it shine on others.

As the sun comes out to shine on you.

Be you.

Walk your walk and talk your talk.

You are wonderful.

You deserve everything.

You are somebody.

STORY

FOURTEEN

CHANGE OUR WORLD

Oh! *What an awesome, beautiful day it is. The birds are chirping their enchanting happy songs. How inspiring it is, such sweet melodies float through my branches. I should admit, on any given morning when I want to sleep in that the birds can be annoying. They have a lot to say to each other, especially when hungry. They give the sweetest gift, a chorus of songs throughout the day. Sing little birds. Do what you are here to do. After a while, there's peaceful silence. Now we sleep. Thank you. I want to sleep. Slowly I drift off to dreamland eventually. Yeah. The flowers are giving off such a wonderful, fabulous fragrance that would have ever entered your nostrils. How gloriously delightful the flowers are. They make you feel so, mmmm, happy! The sun is hot and shining so bright in the sky, too. All the rays are going everywhere like warm fingers touching the morning and my branches. A breeze is blowing at the right temperature, not too cool and all you can say is, "Thank you, Universe."*

The tree felt all was well in the world today. How could it not be?

Walking up the path towards the tree was a young man, his hands in his pockets. He kicked a small pebble as he moved closer to the tree. He was tall, but you would think him to be smaller. The young man's shoulders were slumping down as if he was carrying the weight of the world on them. He walked so slowly as if he was not sure of where he was going. He looked a little lost. The tree did not see which direction he came because he was so caught up in this fabulous day. Weeping Willow could see almost everything around him. It didn't matter if the tree saw him or not, the tree could feel that he was there, and the tree was always so happy to see anyone. Weeping Willow loved to hear their voices as they shared their stories with the tree.

The young man stood quietly, looking at all the beauty around him. Almost in a whisper, he spoke.

Hello Friend.

His voice was choked with emotions. The young man moved closer to the tree as if he had a secret to tell. He put his hand out and reached for the tree.

It is good to touch you again. It has been a long time. It is David, I have come back to see you with a heavy heart. I am so glad you are here in the same place. I have missed the fun and happiness I felt here with you as a child. Here I am, an adult, back to share with you about my short life away from here. The world out there is not always kind. There are people who make it not so easy to live and be happy in our small piece of it.

Suddenly, the young man dropped to his knees. He was crying. He stretched flat out at the base of the tree. He was crying so hard; the tree could feel his chest caving in and out. His fingers dug into the Earth at the base of the tree.

Why are people so mean and devious? I have tried to be good and do the right thing. Some people make others suffer for their pleasure just because they can. They go around bullying the weak and small. They take advantage of people's gentleness and kindness who only want peace. There is such a thing as evil.

Weeping Willow is moved by the young man's tears and words. Dew dripped from the leaves of the tree. Weeping Willow shook as emotions surged through him. Some of the leaves fell on the young man. The young man did not feel them, he was much too distraught engulfed in the pain of his existence. Finally, what seemed like hours, the young man could catch his breath and talk again, clearer this time.

At school and other places, some individuals taunt you, hit you for no other reason than they can. You are not a part of their group. You just don't know! It does not feel good to have your joy taken away day after day. They can make your life a living nightmare. One of the things that hurt the most is them telling lies about you. Make up stories that are not true. You know what's worse? Some people believe the lies and they don't treat you the same. It's a shame. Now, who's the blame for your pain. Growing up can be hard. All you want is to grow up with good friends and good memories. You want to get along with everybody. I admit I was so afraid of being hurt. I am only one person. I know I am not the only one, we all suffer in silence. Dare we speak, we will pay. Some people say, "Be tough." I am one of those people who don't like to fight. I have been through enough of it. No one wants me. I am a nuisance to everyone at home. My family just couldn't see me. I was not asking for anything that is not expected by all children. Where do I go? What do I do? I only want to be cared for.

The young man' s voice was low and raspy.

I looked up to my older siblings. They were much bigger than me. I just wanted to hang out with them. Be friends and be like a loving family. "Talk to me," I begged. They were mean to me and I don't know why. You guys put rips in my heart, and you don't care. You say such mean words, "people don't like you," "we don't want you." Your family can hurt you like no one else can. They can crush your spirit. Make you feel like you are nothing. You start believing it. Young people have courage in dealing with what life has tossed to them. Why is it so hard being good in my neighborhood? The world tries to make you a hoodlum, I am only trying to survive. When you are out on your own, the world can be cruel. You have only a few tools for taking care of yourself. Put out of the nest too soon. Now you fly solo into the cool winds of the streets and rooftop to rooftop. Where will I sleep? You can't weep. People will think you are a creep. You put your few belongings in a sack on your back and walk on. Is this my destiny to go from pillar to post? At this stage in my life, I don't know where I fit in, in what direction I am pointed.

The young man spoke so sadly and slow. The words were difficult for him to say.

No one wants me. I have gone to many places in search of a place to call home. A place where there is protection. A place to feel safe and warm. A place to know that you are wanted and loved. Is there such a place? Will I find it?

The young man reached up and placed his hand on the tree as he continued to lay on the ground at the base of the tree. He curled himself into a ball.

Weeping Willow, I know there is good in the world. Look at me. I know people are good, but I wonder sometimes. My friend, you are still so magnificent and more exceptional. Wow! It is great to be back here with you, talking to you about my life. I am trying to figure out my life while having you listen to my story. I am here to lay my burdens down at your *feet. Just to rest under you and feel the cool of your mighty branches. Yet, they are gentle and comforting. Just being here, everything is clearer.*

Suddenly, the young man sat up.

You know what, my friend? I feel strong, I am strong. I am intelligent. I am a survivor. Yes indeed, I am. Weeping willow, I could tell you more stories, but I will save them for another visit. I will go out into the world and make it a better place. Maybe that is why I am here. Yes! The light I want to see in the world is me. Be a beacon of hope for people. I will do it! Maybe I will start an organization for other people who are going through what I have experienced. Let people know about bullying. The put-downs. The cruelty to one another. The effects it has on another human being. You don't have to be that way. Maybe they will listen. Maybe they will stop. Maybe they will change. Maybe they will be the promoter of peace and healing in all mankind. There's hope.

The young man stood up and danced around the tree.

We have found the answer together. Great one, you listen and have breathed new life into me. We did it! I am so happy I could kiss you.

He did! The tree shook with happy emotions for the young man.

Life is good! I am in a good place now, headed for living life and having much success. I know what I must do. It will be difficult. What isn't when you are just starting from the beginning.

This young man knows who he is now. He will not try and fit in where he is not wanted. He will find his own.

I will not take it anymore. I will not carry the scars of injustice throughout my life. I will be an advocate for people who need help. I will be there.

The young man smiled big coming from deep within himself.

I will show love and kindness to everyone.

He started to walk away from the tree in the direction the tree thinks he came from. The young man turned once more towards the tree.

Maybe I should run. I will use my instincts and I will be triumphant.

He waved goodbye, saying *Hooray! we did it. Thank you!*

The tree could hear the young man in the distance. Then he was gone.

SOMETHING FOR THE PARENTS!

Responsibility. Parents if you bring children into life.

It is your responsibility to take care of them.

Children are a gift from heaven to bring such joy into lives.

They should not go out into the world

before they have the tools to take care of themselves.

Your children will end up in the wrong hands.

The street will devour your precious gifts.

Think.

There is nothing more important than your children.

Parents, protect your children.

If you bring up a child in the right way, with love and understanding

They will not depart from it. They will follow your lead.

You are their first teachers.

Follow the laws of nature.

Some chicks are strong and ready to fly as soon as they can flap their wings.

Some other chicks are slower and need more time.

If you have done your job right with love and patience

They will fly and soar to great heights.

Watch them and you will see.

"I am only the messenger."

Story Fourteen Poetry

"DON'T BULLY"

Do not bully me. Stop hitting me.

Do you know?

I do not like it when you hit me.

I do not like it when you are mean to me.

Defend myself like you.

I depend on you.

Why do you bully me?

Why do you want to cause me pain?

I look at you with such disdain.

You look like me. You eat like me.

You walk like me.

I am you.

How is it working for you being the bully?

Could it be someone is bullying you?

Listen! Do you want it to disappear?

I do.

It can start with you.

Be the change you want for others.

Stop the violence.

Make it happen.

Do not bully!

"A Place To Call Home"

Places everywhere, I see them all around me.

I wish I had a place to call home.

A place of peace.

A place of shelter from the cold

My heart and body long to have a place to call home.

A place to feel safe from harm

from all the struggles of the outside world.

At least until I grow up.

A place to rest at the end of the day

A place where open arms awaits.

A place to fill my tummy with good warm,

hot home cooking. Hmmm. No feeling of hunger.

A place with a mother's sweet smile.

A place with a father's strong voice, and big hugs.

A place where there is kindness and gentleness.

I wish I had a place to call home.

I wait.

STORY

FIFTEEN

AMERICA, AMERICA

A man walked very fast up to the weeping willow tree.

Is he going to pass me by?

The tree was curious, but the man stopped in front of it. His name was Al, and he stood there, looking at the beautiful scenery. He paced back and forth a few times. He pulled out a folder from the case that he was carrying. It had papers in it. He started to speak as if he was making a special speech to an audience of people.

America, America, land of the free. Where there is milk and honey for everyone. Streets are paved with gold. So, I have been told. What are we doing? What have we done? Everything we stand for has gone wrong. Our children's stomachs are empty. They cry out for their mothers and fathers, who have lost their way. The children cry out for help, but you turn a deaf ear. Disgraced and ashamed, I lower my head and cry. Our children are killing each other in the streets. Our children are under all those colored sheets, laying in the alleyways, hallways, and streets for all to see. Are they dying for bread? As you head for your meeting about money and power, is that a siren in the distance? Or the wailing of mothers? Maybe it's the howling of a father's anguish. Their seed, their gift, now silent forever. Their cries are blowing in the wind through the trees. Can you hear them? The trees shake and shutter trying to absorb some of our pain. The trees moved back and forth trying to get our attention. They drop leaves to the ground that are veined with our pain. Look at what you have done to your fellow man. It is just too much to bear. The weight of it all has caused the trees to crack. Now look at what you have done. Nothing can put the trees back together again. Don't despair. There is hope. The trees will bring forth new life. Absolutely.

But where will it end? How will it end? Our women are pushing grocery carts up and down the street. Most of their possessions in them. No place to rest, having to keep pushing, just a little farther. Keep pushing, they do not know where. Maybe a bus stop. America, do we have no heart? Our men are lying stretched out in nooks and alleys exhausted from all the pitfalls in our society. I ask again. What have we done? Power, money, is that all we think about? Stepping on the backs of your fellow man. Where have our values gone? Where is our humanity for each other? Has everything we stand for been shot across the seas, like a rocket aimed for another time zone? Can you not see, they need help?

Toils of today are too heavy to carry. We can't live. Our leaders will find a way. They will hear the cry of their people. Our leaders have to, they must. Reasons for homelessness are as vast as the great canyons of the world and as simple as not giving a helping hand. It is written that I am my brother's keeper. For many, it is difficult to navigate through life dealing with all the obstacles they need to overcome. Life is so unpredictable. Everything can change in an instance. People deal with certain events in life on many levels. Many evolve into a downward spiral. Much help is needed to bring them back.

All of us need to be kind to each other. Everyone should take that step and make a change. I once read something that stuck with me for a long time. Just when a caterpillar gives up on life, it becomes a butterfly. You see, life is full of mysteries. We all can metamorphose into wonderful human beings.

Al stood there with tears running down his face. He wiped them away with the sleeve of his coat.

I didn't expect that to happen. I am so tired too.

The man touched the weeping willow tree.

Can I sit and rest under your cool branches for a little while?

Al gently sat down and stretched out his legs.

Man, this is just what I need.

Al was quiet, just sitting with his papers in his hand. He started to speak again placing the papers beside him.

You know what happened to me the other day? I decided to go shopping for food. I was almost out of food, and I thought it best to have a larger variety. I was in no hurry so I drove slowly looking at the people coming and going. I entered the store, stopped, and realized that I did not make a shopping list.

"Oh! This is going to be fun," I thought to myself.

I walked around in total confusion about what to get. Now that I was in the store nothing was coming to mind. I would love to have a lady to go shopping with. I need a partner in my life. I am wishing and hoping to find her someday soon. What is that song about wishing on a star?

He smiled to himself.

It would be grand to have someone. Why have I waited so long? Maybe it is me, that's why love never works out. Maybe she was here and I let her go. Maybe we are passing each other like two ships at night. Enough of this soul searching. Back to the story. So, I was buying groceries for myself. I was just standing in one of the aisles, thinking, "What should I get?" A woman came up to me, crying heavy tears. She reached out to me.

"Can I hug you?" she asked.

I just stood there. Wow! This shopping trip was getting weirder. My mind was a little cloudy thinking about food, so I was not sure what to make of the situation.

"Sure, you can," I heard myself say.

"Is the world really this bad?" she said in a low voice full of tears.

"It will get better," I assured her as I patted her on the shoulder.

I was near tears myself about now, yet still a little skeptical of this encounter.

"Now don't cry, dry your eyes, put aside your fears. I know for sure a better day is coming. It is blowing in the wind. People will be healed and wake up to what is important."

She looked into my eyes with her eyes that seemed to smile. We parted, saying take care of yourself and be careful out there. She walked down the store aisle, turned to her left, then she was gone. I just stood there thinking. What just happened? Did it happen? Am I hallucinating? You have those times in your life, where you question yourself. I touched my face and the remnant of water from her tears lingered on my cheek. Was it just a memory from another time? I looked around me. I was alone in that aisle. It did happen, Weeping Willow. Yeah.

The tree shook a little, moved by this quiet man. The tree moved just enough to cause a cool breeze to brush over Al.

Hmmmm, that is nice. I needed to do this, come and visit you, my friend. Have a conversation and rest my weary self.

The man was quiet now, looking out beyond the tree. The tree was not sure what to think of this man. The tree felt something for him. Was the man one of the children who played here many years ago? The man didn't say.

I think he called me the friend; Weeping Willow imagined. ***I feel that I know him. This man has so much on his mind to consider.***

Weeping Willow heard Al whisper to himself. A short time later, the man stood and brushed the leaves off his clothes.

I have a long way to go. There is much to be done. I will do my part to help change this situation in our land. Someone will do it. Am I the one? I don't know. Maybe I am just the one to do it. Why not?

Al looked at the tree as if waiting for an answer. Al reached his hand out and touched the tree, leaving his imprint on the tree as if conveying a message. Maybe a message to himself from the tree.

I know you understand. I am going now to get started.

He walked away hurriedly. Then he was gone.

Story Fifteen Poetry

"MAKE A DIFFERENCE"

The change is in you. It starts with each one of us.

Live life simply. Do not take more than you need.

We are destroying Mother Earth.

Let's save our world. Let's save each other.

Our time is now.

We have the greatest technology in the world.

Are we happy? More everything.

Yet people go hungry.

We have lost what is most valuable in life.

Love for one another.

Yet People go hungry.

Why? We had the sixties and the

Seventies. They sang about peace and love.

Respect your brother. Do the right

Things. Here we are singing the same songs.

When will they ever learn?

Let us join hands in brotherhood.

We can live out our destiny in joy and peace.

~ The Messenger

STORY

SIXTEEN

Hopes And Dreams At The Casino

Mister OG, you finally made it over here.

The tree was excited as the gentleman approached the area where the tree was rooted and standing tall, watching. The tree knew him as Mister OG. Weeping Willow liked that name for him. The name just fits him. They had been friends for a long time. Weeping Willow smiled, as he thought of Mister OG fondly.

Mister OG, I can see you in the distance, walking at a fast pace.

Mister OG placed one hand on the tree for support.

Wow! I am off my regular schedule today and trying to make up for lost time. I did not take my time getting here to visit you. It was a fast-paced walk over here. I try to keep in shape.

Mister OG smiled to himself, thinking of a future event that stayed heavy on his mind.

I need to catch my breath. It's a long trip to get here on foot. I guess some days are better than others in the exercise department. Weeping Willow, I feel great. I take care of myself. Let me rest here under your cool branches for a little while before I continue my journey. It's such a beautiful day to be out and about. Yeah.

Mister OG said this with such glee and happy enthusiasm. The tree could feel his emotions.

How are you doing today my friend?

Mister OG patted the tree. Weeping Willow shook a little, letting leaves fall on him. I can tell by your display of happiness that you are alright. The tree has been visited many times over the years by Mister OG. He lived in the area not far from this beautiful place. Somewhere out there in the distance. Mister OG told the tree everything about his life. He shared his most precious secrets. The tree was considered one of his buddies. Weeping Willow was always there to listen. Mister OG felt positive about life, after baring his soul to the tree. Mister OG got all the answers he needed. Go figure. He just felt so much better about everything, life was a little clearer. Mister OG couldn't explain it. Why try? He's just happy that this tree is here for him. Mister OG was sure there are others, but for now, he has the tree to himself.

Thank you, Weeping Willow.

Every Saturday, Mister OG stopped by to see the tree on his way to the casino. Mister OG never missed a Saturday. Today was special. It was a holiday. Mister OG carried a small American flag in his pocket. He spoke with conviction in his voice.

This is where I belong. I love my country. I have been all over the world. When I am away, I long for home.

Mister OG was in the military for years. He talked about his many adventures with many of his buddies from all over the U.S.A. They had so much fun and they did everything together.

"Many of them are gone now," Mister OG whispered, not wanting to say it out loud.

He missed them very much. They would meet every year in different places all over the country. The men never miss a year. It was their tradition. They had agreed many years ago to always be a part of each other's lives. Support each other in all the twists and turns of life. They were there for all the special events, dating, marriages, children, graduations, divorces, and other events. Mister OG was there. He traveled to them anywhere. no matter how far they were. All they had to do was call.

A look came into his eyes. Mister OG was quiet. He appeared to be a little sad. A tear rolled down his cheek, the tree was sure of it.

Maybe thinking about his friends and the bond they had, conjured up so many emotions.

Weeping Willow heard many stories from Mister OG about his life. But one story was very dear to Mister OG's heart. At that moment Mister, OG started to laugh and sounded very much alive again.

Let me tell you about what happened last Saturday at the casino.

I know. Here we go again. '

The tree knew what was coming. The tree was excited to go on an adventure with Mister OG.

Mister OG was taking fast and steady steps walking up to the casino's doors that open at will for him to enter. There was much excitement in the air. Mister OG loved all of it here at the casino. But every week, he tells himself, "This is it! I am going to stay away from here". He can't stay away, and there he was again. He looked around, thinking "Maybe she will be here."

That same familiar smell hit his nose. The smell of smoke and money. Mister OG's nose flared as his memory made him think of her. The smell of expensive perfumes that she has on, ignited his brain. Jasmine and vanilla are so sweet. Lips parting to speak, red as two rose petals began to speak his name. He remembers a time before, a life, yet it seems like yesterday.

Will I ever forget? Can I forget?

She is there always in his thoughts, smiling that beautiful smile with teeth so perfect. Full of invites, so white like new piano keys.

Dazzling. She lights up a room and I am warmed by her rays that run through me, from my head to my toes. She has my heart. I am lost in her world of her. My imagination takes over once again. I can hear her saying to me, "Mister OG you are mine alone. I love you, only you. I want only you."

Mister OG realized he is thinking too much. He was standing in the middle of the casino leading to the restaurant. That's where he was headed. He looked for his spot, the table where he usually sat, moving slowly, looking around for her. Mister OG's table was open so he sat down. One of the waitresses walked over to his table.

"It's good to see you."

"Thank you."

"Can I take your order?"

"Yes." Mister OG ordered the same meal as usual.

"Are you ok Mister OG?"

"Yes," he smiled to himself.

He was thinking of a secret that only he carries. A love that should have been. A love that is never forgotten. A love from his youth that haunts him, even in his dreams. Mister OG thought of her walk. What a walk. His heart skipped a beat thinking of her movements. A beautiful portrait in motion. The swing of her hips, inviting you to wish for closeness. The desire to encircle her in your arms. A wonderful fascinating woman that has been blessed with all that nature has to give. Perfection. She was so sweet and charming. To know her is to love her.

What would I give to love her? All that I have. She will not take anything from me. It's destiny for me to wait.
Mister OG's food arrived as he was lost in thought. He did not see the person who served him, only the smell of the food that serenaded his nose. He thought about how pleasant she could be. She would love this

meal. He slowly picked up his fork. and puts it in his mouth. Eating was something to do as he waited. He took the time to savor every delicious bite of his food.

I guess I was hungry.

Mister OG continued to think to himself.

I asked myself over the years, why do I go through life longing for a love that I can't have?

Alas, something dawned on him.

There is always hope. You should never give up, then it happened! I ran into her by accident. Man! I could not believe it. Wow! I could hardly speak. My words were stuck in my throat. At last, I could speak and my words came out so fast. She affects me that way and today was no different.

"Hello! How are you?" What he really wanted to say was, "Let's go. I want to be alone with you." But, he didn't.

I was going to another city, but after meeting her I changed my mind, and I'm glad I did.

"Where have you been?"

Mister OG's mouth would not stop asking her questions. He was just so happy for this chance encounter.

"I just can't believe it!" he repeated.

She was smiling, looking at him, trying to answer all the questions he asked.

"How is life treating you?"

She could not get a word out.

"Life is good!" she was finally able to reply.

"How have you been?" Mister OG was trying to think of what more to say. Anything to keep her here with him longer.

All the feelings were still there. Does she have a clue?

"It is so good to see you again. It's been a while."

She concurred and was also talking with excitement and laughing all the while. Mister OG wanted to kiss her. But he kept his temptation in check.

Oh! That laugh of hers evoked such a happy feeling in me. That's how it is.

"Yes, sweetie, life is good!" she repeated. "The Universe has been good to me. I hope for you also, my friend."

There she goes again with that friendship stuff.

Mister OG spoke with enthusiasm, "Now that we are in contact again, can I see you sometime?"

"Yes, you can. Where?"

"At the casino." This was the first place that came to his mind. "I go there every Saturday."

"Maybe, I will try," she said with a smile. Suddenly she started to walk away. "I have to go now."

"Wait!" Mister OG wanted to talk more, just a little while longer. "You will come, right?!"

By then, she was already well on her way. Maybe she heard me. I don't know. She waved her hand as she walked *away, out of my life again.*

He could do nothing.

"Goodbye," he whispered to himself.

She was far off in the distance. Mister OG smiled to himself.

I will see her again. Maybe she will come to the casino. Maybe she will think of me, waiting for her, a love unfilled. I loved you then, I love you now. We dated. We had great times together. Maybe I assumed too much. We were young and free. Maybe I was her growing tree. This time maybe she will see that we can be more than friends. I know she loves another. He has her heart, mind, and body. She told me this years ago. I don't care. It's my time to be with you. Give me a chance to prove my love for you. I will love you like no other for the rest of our lives. I will give you all that is in my power. It is not too late, feel me. Do not let my love slip away again. I know you love another. Maybe she will fit me in her schedule one of these days. My life has been full, a part of the great spectrum in life.

Mister OG's mind went back to another time. They were on the dance floor, grooving to the beat. They danced so well together. He took her in his arms. There were only the two of them on the dance floor, dancing around and around, oblivious to the world around them. Or at least Mister OG was oblivious anyway, lost in her gaze and rhythm. They danced all night.

He pleaded with her. "Please be mine. I love you. Can't you see it in my eyes? Can you feel the passion in my body? I feel so alive with you."

Mister OG tried to kiss her lips that have the look of the sweetest strawberry, beckoning to be kissed by his lips. They quiver at the thought of their union. Such pleasure is not too much to ask for in this life. Is it? She turned away, laughing, and disappeared into the darkness.

Ching! went the sounds of machines with lights flashing. Mister OG realized the noise was the slot machines at the casino.

"Oh my goodness! I am in the casino!" He shook his head. "I have been asleep at the casino. Dreaming all this time."

He looked around with tears in his eyes. No one bothered to wake him. Maybe they wanted him to rest. He looked around again. He was alone at his table. The dream was so real. Mister OG decided to get up and play the machines. He stopped after walking only a few feet.

Maybe she will come. If I walk away, I will miss her.

He returned to his table.

What can I do? Only wait. If she arrives, I know she will be looking for me. I can't take that chance of missing her.

Ching! Chang! went the sound of others playing, having a great time. Mister OG looked out over the crowd once more, hoping to see her.

She will come walking over to me. Give me a big hug and kiss and just hold me.

He smiled at the thought of it.

I continue to wait. Forced to come every Saturday by my heart and body that longs to be satisfied. Oh, love of so long ago. Am I being foolish?

After a few minutes more, he walked toward the door taking slow easy steps. All around him, people were talking and laughing. They were yelling with excitement. Machines were going off and lights were flashing. Games were being announced on the televisions. Yet, Mister OG does not look back this time. He thinks only of next Saturday.

Maybe. Just maybe.

Mister OG sat at the base of the tree and shook his head.
It was all a dream. Can you believe it, Weeping Willow, a dream?

Mister OG laughed out loud. He was quiet for a moment then spoke slowly.

Everyone should have something to live for. Looking forward to a special day makes you want to move. Even if it's a hope and dream. There are many changes in this universe, but the need for contact with someone or something, that never changes. It is the base of our existence. Yeah.

Mister OG looked at the time.

I can't be late!

Mister OG is not sure if he was dreaming under the tree or telling the story to the tree.

Thanks for listening to me.

He gave the tree a quick pat. He picked up his pace as he walked away, now fully rested. Mister OG turned once more and waved.

Luck is on my side today. I can feel it.

Then he was gone.

Story Sixteen Poetry

"RAINBOW"

At the end of my rainbow, all I want is you.

You are the colors dazzling in my eyes.

Leaving me in a daze.

There is one color I want to see in the rainbow

your bright smile.

That is my sunshine, it warms me all over.

Hide my feelings for you.

Never.

I plead to you.

Forget about the pot of gold,

that might be over the rainbow.

I am here.

I want to fold you in my arms.

Keep you from harm.

Fill you up with all my charms.

Can you hear me?

You are my rainbow.

STORY

SEVENTEEN

Bell

Someone is slowly walking up the path with a look of sadness on her face. It's the lady from a few days ago here to see me again.

Weeping Willow gently moved from side to side creating a cool breeze just in case she needed it. The day was a hot one. The lady sat down under the tree looking out into the distance saying not a word for a short time. Suddenly she spoke.

Weeping Willow, I am back so soon to share with you my story today because of a little hurt to my heart. It's a story that happened many years ago when I was a young child. It is about the power of good intentions, love, and giving back to a blessed heart. My mother said she asked the Universe to watch over her children. There were occasions where her request was granted.

Blue sky with streaks of white clouds hovering in the horizon with bright sun rays shining through touching you with a warm rainbow of color. A day you think about all winter as you anticipate the lovely days of summer. It is here and you revel in it with such boisterous festivity for a day perfect as this one. Freedom to do whatever is your heart's desire.

I remember Bell. Big black and brown eyes, watching us as we played in the backyard. He was as white as the snow on a snow-capped mountain top from head to hoofs. He was one of the Universe's remarkable creations. Bell was as impressive as any thoroughbred show horse that has marched out on a field to be awarded a medal.

Bell just happened to live on a farm where he was adored and loved. He would prance back and forth in his corral. Bell had an overwhelming presence and an air of royalty about him. He was conveying to all, "Look at me, I am something special," and he was. Bell stood proud and very still sometimes looking at us with a little curiosity.

It was not every day he saw children running around the farm. We were visiting from the city to see our grandparents. I am not sure what Bell thought of all these little people.

My grandparents had many other animals on the farm. Lots of chicken, baby chicks, pigs, piglets, ducks, baby ducks, cows, calves, rabbits, and many more. These were our favorites. We all had a great time exploring the farm. It was just lovely. We played and held many of the smaller animals. We often put them against our faces. How soft and cuddly they were and happy for all the attention we gave them.

It was such a beautiful day on one of our trips around the farm to play. I had the charge of my little sister to make sure she did not get into anything. We were running, skipping, and laughing until our stomachs hurt. Being happy as can be, free to roam. I was smelling the beautiful flowers, distracted for a minute. There were a variety of flowers and they were everywhere. I don't know what happened, but I got caught up in the moment.

I love nature. I felt so peaceful to be a part of something bigger than myself. One occasion we got lost in the field of flowers on purpose. Everyone was looking for us. We could hear them calling our names. We did not move as we were gazing up at the beautiful blue sky, daydreaming, which was something I was known for.

Smiling and feeling so good, reality hit me like a slap on the back. I lost sight of my little sister. Oops! Where is she? Frantic, my head was going in every direction. I ran through the field searching for her. Where is she? Just as I turned by the barn, I saw her roll into Bell's pen. I screamed "no" but it was too late, she was already in there.

My other siblings watched in horror as they were too far away to do anything. Bell was watching my sister's quick movements. Suddenly, Bell stood up on his two back legs, higher and higher up. In an instant, without thinking, I rolled under the corral, grabbed my little sister, and we both rolled back under the corral fast. Bell came down on all fours as we cleared shaking his head and making horse sounds.

To this day, I am not sure if Bell was startled by our fast movements or if he was going to stomp us. I'm sure glad we don't know. I never got a bad feeling about Bell, but we were told to stay away from the area. "Look at the horse but do not touch."

As we lay on the ground trying to catch our breath, I was realizing what almost happened. Bell stood quietly looking at us. My little sister laughed, happy about the game she thought we were playing. She did not know the danger we were in. Animals are very smart. Maybe it is possible that Bell knew we belonged to our grandparents.

Everyone came running over including our brother and sister. I couldn't speak or say a word. I just held her in my arms and took in her happy sounds. She was safe with us now. All I could think about was how we both could have been hurt. Wow! We stood up brushing the dirt off our clothing and turned to look at Bell. We met each other's gaze looking into each other's eyes, and the mind smiled a thank you.

I didn't tell any of the adults about it and I don't think anyone else mentioned the incident. It was very important for me to have the trust of my parents and grandparents. I was the dependable one, the reliable one, the thinker, the peacemaker. I had to hang on to these titles.

They were all so proud of me in every way. Father and Mother agreed that I was good. They told me so on numerous occasions. Trouble was something I stayed away from. I was shy and I did not say much. They made me feel like I was on top of the world, that I was somebody. They made my heart smile. Little old me could mean so much to somebody. That is something special. Every child needs to feel that they are special and loved. When I think back about the incident, I realize that I was little too.

My sister and I are adults now with our own families, moving forward enjoying life to the max. My sister relocated to another state with her husband and children. We are close, and I miss her. My sister is my friend and I treasure her. We talk on the phone about everything for hours. Getting a clear picture of what is going on in each of our lives. She brings joy and much knowledge to our family.

On this one particular day, she started telling me stories about her many adventures in the south. To have lived through it is something to tell others. Maybe she will write a book. The stories were about her wit and survival in an unfamiliar place. The words just came out of my mouth after all this time and the many conversations we have had. The incident was let out into the Universe once more to the benefactor of the Universe's gift of life. I was excited to tell her.

"I have never told you this. Your life was saved by me when we were little." I recalled the story about Bell to her.

"We both could have been seriously hurt or worse; killed." She was quiet for a second or two. Then she spoke.

"You never told me about this incident before or anyone else."

"There were other siblings there. They know, they witnessed it. We just never talked about it. I don't know why."

Weeping Willow, what hurt me deeply was that my sister could not take in what I was saying. I know after all these years it sounded unreal. Why bring it up now? But she should know that I always speak the truth. It happened exactly as I stated it. Another sister was there to witness the near-death experience. She saw it all as it happened. Weeping Willow, my sister got very quiet and changed the subject.

All these years, I have carried the incident with me locked in a box with my treasured memories of a past gone by. Why do children keep secrets? There are a number of reasons or maybe they just simply forget. There are so many obstacles to cross getting to adulthood and it is not always easy to remember it all.

Thinking about it today, both our angels were watching over us. Was it the breath of the Universe blowing the wind that pushed us gently but swiftly as we rolled to safety? There are events in this life that boggles the imagination. Mysteries that cannot be explained. I did go to my sister who was with me that day and asked her if she remembered the incident with Bell. She smiled and said yes. She repeated exactly what took place without me saying a word.

"So, you see it did happen. It was not a dream," I verified with her.

I did not know it then, how could I? But there was humanitarian work to do in both our futures. My journey has taken me into avenues to help many people in need. I had a dream to touch the lives and hearts of many. To make a difference. Bring joy out of pain, bring happiness, not sadness. My dreams were fulfilled many times over as a wife, mother, teacher, peacemaker, and caregiver. This was my mission in life. It is written and so shall it be. I embraced it all.

The irony of it is my sister is also in humanitarian work. No way did we know how our paths would lead us to change and be an influence in many lives. My sister has made this a better world for many. I salute and applaud you, sister. Keep up the good work of changing people's lives. I don't mean to be repetitive, but life truly is a great mystery. There are many events about it that we do not understand.

Thinking back to the incident, it is an awe moment for me. How did I do it? How did I save her? It is okay if she does not believe me, Weeping Willow. Every day we should give thanks for what we have. Life has been good to me and mine. Many good people have touched my life as I have walked this journey. Most of all, I remember the horse named Bell. Immortalized in these few pages of my life forever. Oh! how times go by so quickly.

It's time for me to go. I am at peace now.

The lady spoke out loud into the wind. She got up and placed her hand on the tree.

Thank you.

She smiled, walked away. Then she was gone.

STORY

EIGHTEEN

Sweet Days Of Summer

Weeping Willow stretched reaching upward as far as possible. He is alone again, gazing, looking out over the houses, hills, and the valleys green and beautiful. Even the flowers that take your breath away were visible in all the colors of life, blues, whites, reds, yellows, browns, oranges, and purples that are dark and black. There are too many to name, just imagine. Lovely houses with gardens, full of vegetables and fruits that filled the air with delight. Animals live and thrive there. What a wonderful place to live. Weeping Willow looked up and down many roads as far as he could see. From where he was rooted, that was quite a distance. Many cars, trucks, buses, all full of people in them coming and going.

Honk! Honk! Beep!

Many of them coming so close to Weeping Willow look his way with a wave and a smile, pointing, only to pass hurriedly by. They don't know the hurt and pain down to his roots that extend far into the Earth, hidden from the world to hide some of his personal torment.

Where is everyone going so fast?

Vehicles are going at many different speeds.

Slow down! You are moving too fast. You will get to your destinations sooner or later. Don't be in such a hurry. Just take it slow, please.

Weeping Willow's dew started to fall thinking about what could happen.

I wish I could go. If only for a little while. I know this is where I belong but I get curious thinking about what is beyond my world. This is my home. It's where I belong, but I get to peek at the world beyond here when I stretch. Yeah. I have not forgotten the stories of others. I am humbled and grateful. There is so much beauty here around me as far as the eyes can see.

Weeping Willow moved back and forth stretching, watching in this inspiring place, welcoming others as they stop to rest and tell their many stories as they travel through life.

I am honored to give comfort to those who seek it.

All summer long, the family was here in this place Weeping Willow calls home.

"I love it here," Harmony would say.

Granny also lived here in one of the beautiful homes. Granny's house was so much fun and Harmony said they are loved and wanted here. There are plenty of hugs and kisses. Such good food from Granny's kitchen.

Can you smell it? Here they come up the dirt drive to see Granny and all their friends. Everyone is waiting. The family from the city. All the children squealed, their city friends. Everyone is jumping up and down happy to see their wonderful friends. As soon as they reach Granny's porch. The children run to her. They love their Granny.

Weeping Willow was watching from afar.

Granny is also happy to see her daughter's children. She does not get to see them often.

"We love you Granny, but we want to play. Tell Harmony we are at the tree when she arrives."

Harmony is one of the children's cousins from the city. Harmony was going to ride with them but she had obligations to take care of in other places. She will meet them here later. All the children go in the direction of the tree, singing, clapping their hands. All the adults say at once, "Come in soon." as they all go into the house.

They loved that tree. The children all run and hug him.

"We missed you. How glad we are to see you. We think of you all the time, at our house in the city. In the city so far away from here," they say All the children hold hands as they dance around the tree. You could hear their giggles for miles around.

Sweet summer days. The birds sang lovely songs as the children lay beneath Weeping Willow's branches. They shade the children from the hot sun after long hours of play. A gentle breeze from the wind made the branches move back and forth softly cooling the children.

"We all should be home before dark," one of the children says.

Weeping Willow did not want the children to go. They all had too much fun throughout the day. The children wave many times as they disappear into the sunset. Weeping Willow moved his branches.

I wish for the night. Then the daylight will come again and the happiness they bring will start over again.

In the morning, as the rooster crows, the children run to the tree.

"This is Harmony. She was late yesterday and did not make it here to see you. Harmony can play guitar so beautifully. She is going to the University to study music this year. Harmony is a natural. Music is one of the arts she lives for. Harmony is going to be one of the great guitar players. Harmony creates beautiful music for us as we dance and play."

The children excitedly spoke over one another as they introduced Harmony to Weeping Willow.

They played for a long time. Harmony even played and danced for a few minutes with them.

How nice.

Weeping Willow likes her too. She smiles and laughs out loud with such happiness. Weeping Willow's leaves fell on them. He shook with happiness. For many days, the children played. Harmony came with the children to visit with Weeping Willow all summer long. She would play music that lit them up like firebugs in the night.

Weeping Willow was fond of having them all there with him. He was very happy. They all had so much fun running, rolling in the grass near Weeping Willow. Such delights in the sweet days of summer.

The fun went on for weeks. Weeping Willow was happy more than anyone knew. The next day, the children did not show up. Without a word. Weeping Willow knew the family would disappear each summer after being there for weeks. The family would return to Granny's house after rains of winter. Not this time. Many summers would come and go. The family did not return.

I miss them so.

The tree can only sway back and forth, reaching upward as far as he could. He dives into his memories and remembers all he can.

Dragonflies dance and circle around her. Butterflies land gently on her hand, just to touch her. Sweet honeybees and wasp want to sting her. Buzzing, swarming, and flying around her hair. The birds fly around and tweet sweet songs as they serenade her. We all wanted to be close to her.

Many nights, he looked up at the stars thinking of her music. The dew would pop out on his leaves and branches. He would weep.

Where is she? She will never come here again.

This made Weeping Willow weep. He wept and wept and he could not stop. The weight of his tears forced his leaves to droop towards the Earth. His tears drop to the Earth around him. When it rains, the tears flow throughout the land traveling where Weeping Willow can't go. He thought maybe she would step in a rain puddle and see a diamond-shaped teardrop.

On any rainy day, if you're outside, step in a puddle of rain, and you too might see a diamond-shaped teardrop.

STORY

NINETEEN

THE REVEAL

S uddenly, one day there she was. Weeping Willow was sure it was Harmony. She was taller, but it was her.

I knew she might come back one day. I can't wait to see her and all her friends and family. I will welcome her back.

It was such a time of joy for the tree. Harmony had been on tour with other groups. They had traveled far. She needed to rest. The family felt Granny's place would be perfect. Here they are so Harmony can get much-needed rest and relaxation. Weeping Willow could hear Harmony's music playing in the air as she performed a short concert for her family. It sounded great. He waited for her all day and late into the evening. She did not show up to visit the tree.

Where is she? What is the matter? I do not care. I will go to her. Yes! That is what I will do. The sky that night is full of stars twinkling in the sky like glitter against the dark sky. It wraps me in its warm blackness. My friend, the moon, appears big and bright and bold in the sky. This is a sign that tonight is the time to do it.

That night, as she slept with her window open, Weeping Willow climbed the high balcony ever so quietly and through the open window. He looked at her. She was sleeping so peacefully. He decided to stay the night and watch over her. He would be there when she woke up in the morning. She would feel so protected that she was being watched over.

Weeping Willow could have waited until the next day to see if she would come and see the tree, but it's too late now.

As the rays of the sun reached through her window, the warm rays touched him, giving him the courage to stay. Trying hard not to shake, he could only watch. Harmony woke up slowly, stretching, rubbing her eyes as she looked around the room. Weeping Willow's whole existence is shattered in the blink of an eye. Harmony started to scream. She rubbed her eyes viciously.

"What! Am I still asleep! I am dreaming for sure!"

Reality set in. Harmony started to scream again as she looked around her room. There were tree branches in all his beauty on all the walls, and around her bed.

I was careful not to touch her. Only let her see the real me. Reveal me as never before. Why is she so frightened? I will not harm you.

The tree shook gently, leaves going everywhere.

I have missed you. I come in peace. You played beautiful music for me not so long ago.

Reality set in for Weeping Willow as well. Her screams could be heard from far away. He recoiled in terror and pure shock. He retracted his branches back through the window, the way he came in, this time, much faster. Harmony kept screaming with her hands over her eyes. She sat there in bed afraid to uncover them. Afraid of what might still be there. Harmony's parents came charging into her room.

"What is the matter, my love! Why are you screaming?"

She could only point in the direction of her window.

Finally, she whispered, "The tree."

"You were having a bad dream," her parents tried to console her.

She moved her head from side to side, pointing at the tree.

"The tree is quite a distance from your window, Harmony."

She pointed to all the leaves on her bedroom floor.

Weeping Willow swayed back and forth, hurt and dismayed by her reaction. How could it all go so wrong? She was his friend. She played beautiful music for him all summer long. They had a friendship that was pure and innocent. He was sure she liked him. What happened? She had the look of terror in her eyes. The sound of terror in her voice. Weeping Willow will never forget this day. It made him very sad, leaves drooping more with tears on his branches.

Does anyone weep for me? Maybe the sky and heaven above. If only I wasn't a tree.

He was so sad.

Late morning came. He was watching now, afraid to move. Frozen in shock. People were coming out of the house very fast. Running around the car. Stacking their luggage in the back seat and trunk of their car. The family didn't say a word. No words were spoken. They got in the car. Harmony did not look in the direction of the tree. They drove off fast and dirt filled the air. Weeping Willow could not see the car until they were far in the distance. Then they were gone.

If you pass a weeping willow tree, be kind. Give the tree a hug. If you listen close, you can hear him weeping.

Story Nineteen Poetry

"I Thought"

You got me.

Why am I so blue?

I thought rainy days and nights,

would not be missed wrapped in your arms that

Encompass me as rings surround our fingers.

I thought your reflection and protection

Would be forgotten.

I thought a feeling of pride,

that abide in the knowledge of total

Love

really belonging somewhere, to someone.

I thought I could survive without your smile.

It made me feel so alive,

the way you held my hand.

The smell of heavy musk

butterfly kisses so sweet, so gentle

on the front of my head.

Your hand in the center of my back. I thought.

I thought I could lock up my heart and throw away the key.

Those wonderful feelings of love

Keep tugging at my heart.

At night when all is quiet,

and I do not hear your heart beating.

It is difficult to

Sleep without your warmth next to me.

All these things I thought I could live

without.

I miss you.

Sleep now

you are thinking too much.

"Blackness Is My Cover"

In the midnight hour thinking about my honey.

Darkness encircles me as a beautiful warm coat.

All the lights have gone out.

The night is what I wait for,

blackness is my friend.

It wraps me in softness.

I feel that everything is going to be alright.

It hides my tears as they drop like water from a

leaf on a tree after a heavy rain

so slowly onto my pillow

Memories are so fresh, so pure,

so real the hurt that melts from my heart.

At night as the moon peeks through my window.

Peace be still my heart.

Tomorrow the sun will come out

I will welcome it.

A cool breeze suddenly, touch me like gentle fingers of yours.

I think of your bright smile,

the glow in your eyes.

The sound of your laughter.

The feel of your hands.

The memories of hot kisses that still burn on my cheeks.

Branded there forever

As I remember the heat of your touches.

I say peace be still my heart

I remember the pleasure of our time together

it was so good in the daylight.

Now that you are gone.

I long for the black of night.

STORY

TWENTY

LITTLE MARINE

O nce upon a time, there was a little girl named Marine. She was meeting her grandmother for the first time on her mother's side. It was a little scary for Marine and her sisters. The children were told many distinct stories about their grandmother. Marine and her sister were informed that the family came here many years ago to see Granny. Marine was a baby at the time. Her mother said she was a beautiful baby. She had cute, soft, plump cheeks, you just wanted to kiss them. She was such a good baby. A precious bundle of joy.

"Well, you can say that again," Marine's dad said as he laughed.

He loved his children very much and was so proud to be called Dad. He had moved to the city when he was very young. He loved everything about it. The tall buildings that seem to reach into the clouds. All the noise of cars, trucks, and people; all the sounds you hear in the city were awesome to him.

"This is where I belong, with all this excitement," he used to say, so he stayed there in the big city.

Granny lived on a farm on the edge of a big city. The children were informed that Granny didn't like the city. It was just too busy and had too many people. She rarely visited there, only if she had to for something special. She loved the country life. It's the only life for her. She will live there always. She knows everything about farming. Granny and Grandad grew and harvested most of their needs, which were modest. They were happy and lived by the laws of nature; use and take only what you need to live. The simple life. That was a different day and time.

Now, the city has come to Granny's. In their area now are highways and byways nearby. This was the same long highway that Marine and her family drove on a stretch for miles and miles that brought them to Granny's house. The highway going past their farm keeps going further and further into the many cities.

Who is this larger than life figure of a woman whom everyone has heard so much about? Such wonderful stories, which were all true and verified by Marine's mother.

Granny knew how to farm as good as any man. She loved it. She was not afraid of hard work. Another trait passed on to me. Granny was so healthy. She could have been a doctor. She had a simple cure for everything. "It's all here on the farm," she would say. There were many stories about her cooking. Granny was a true chef. She could cook better than anyone around her. Maybe the entire county. Granny could whip up a meal before you walked out of the kitchen, turned around, and walked back in the kitchen. She was that remarkable. Granny's meals were made fresh. Right off the farm. Delicious. It would just make you want to hug her and we did.

Marine's mother always gave such great praise and compliments regarding her mother and father. Marine's grandfather was very quiet, didn't talk much. He let Granny handle almost all the business. She knew how. He trusted and loved her. Marine heard that Granny is sweet and sour, though mostly sweet. She is very strong and knows her way around. Yes. She is a smart woman. No one could get over on her, no one. She is the one who runs the house. Granddad runs the farming, but she is at his side. She doesn't take nonsense from anyone. She is very fair. Granny can size you up, just by looking at you. She was something else. Many other houses were around in the area.

"Granny's was the largest one," Marine's parents said. "Just look for the house with the large columns out front," they would say

The excitement was building as we rode on. It was getting real to all of us children. There was much chatter about what to expect from us. We were all very well behaved. Our parents did an exceptional job raising us. Just awesome! We would not be a problem for anyone. Granny will be very proud of her grandchildren. We were city kids on our way to experience the country life that we have heard so much about. We were so happy just thinking about it. We wanted to hurry up and get there!

Marine's father had this slick new shiny black car with leather seats that felt like her father's big leather chair. The car was as smooth as gliding on a tame sea. He wanted a new car for a long time and worked very hard to get it.

He told us many times that he was going to get it. "Just you all wait and see!" he would tell us. Guess what! He did, to our delight. It was beautiful. Dad was so proud of himself. You could see it in his eyes as he showed it to us and placed his hands on his car. This was quite an accomplishment and he knew it.

He was so excited to show it to Marine's family.

We children settled down and gazed out the window. There was so much to see as we drove along the highway. Our little eyes were full of the sight of spectacular fields and fields of green meadows with hints of all or many colors of the rainbow. There was not a cloud in the big gorgeous sky. Sun rays came through the car's windows like a warm blanket that covered us. There was a cool breeze blowing on us. Hmmmm. Such a feeling of anticipation of the many adventures in this new world.

Marine's parents came from this world. Her parents are wonderful people, so there's no doubt that this farm was a great place.

"We are almost there!" Marine's father exclaimed.

Their mother just smiled her usual beautiful smile. The children just looked at each other in complete silence. You could hear dragonfly wings flapping and the quiet hum of the car's motor. Oh boy! The children were so nervous, yet excited at the same time. Adults do not realize what large figure they appear to children. Well, maybe they do as they were once children.

The children were all asking questions at once, "Should we call her Granny on our first meeting? Can we hug them right away?"

Marine's mother replied, "Just do what you feel. Be your sweet selves. I am sure everything will come to you children. Don't worry, it will be just fine."

We turned off the highway onto this driveway that to us children seem endless. We spotted delicious fruits and vegetables out in the fields as far as our eyes could see. Beautiful trees lined the roadway all the way up to the house. At long last, there it was. This huge house with large columns, just as our parents had described it. The front porch stretched from one end of the house to the other. Wow! It was something to see. In other words, stupendous in all its uniqueness. We children had no idea it would be so grand.

Granny and Grandad were there standing on the porch in front of the stairs leading up to them. They were smiling big, with arms open to us. We jumped out of the car, some of us went to Granny's arms first. The others to Grandad's arms. Everyone was so glad to see each other.

Marine's mother made the introductions, "Here are your grandchildren at long last." She said each of their names.

"Welcome my little ones. Granny has waited a long time to see you, children. At long last you are here," Granny greeted.

Granny had an accent. It was very nice and different. We didn't care at that moment. Granny's arms felt so good. We felt that we've always known her. What a delightful, warm welcome.

"Come on in. Let granny show you your rooms."

Wow! It is so warm and cozy. A large fireplace was in the first room we entered. On the other end was a large bed with a beautiful brass headboard and frame with a lovely comforter in a floral print of many colors. Marine was so excited.

"Oh! That is where I got the love of flowers from. You, Granny," Marine noted. Everyone laughed.

"Rugs on the hardwood floors, right, to keep your feet warm." Granny smiled at us as she showed us around. *"No jumping on the beds, right?"* She winked, knowing that we would. Maybe.

Granny had such a kindness in her voice. She loved us already. We children could feel it. Everything was so clean. Granny loved a clean house, but it should have the ambiance of being lived in.

"Come on with Granny," she said as she ventured into a very impressive kitchen.

It had a large stove with big pots on it. There were different sizes for many dishes. The kitchen was clean and everything in place. It also had large windows. Granny loved to watch everything around outside.

"It's so beautiful, you just feel happy to be alive," she explained. I just love to smell the clean. Do you know that cleanliness is next to Godliness?" Granny took a deep breath. That's Granny's way.

"Changing the subject, you all can eat anytime you like. I know you are starving. You all have come a long way. I have made something special for you."

The kitchen was so delightful and smelled good. Everyone's tummy was ready for food.

"Dinner is ready," Granny turned to us smiling.

There was plenty for all. There was no problem when it came to food. Marine and her sisters love almost everything in the food chain. Oh no, their parents had no trouble getting them to eat. Their parents fed them what they liked.

They made everything that was cooked to our liking. I mean everything tasted good to us anyway.
They never forced Marine and her sisters to eat anything they didn't like.

"They will grow into it later. These unfamiliar foods will become familiar when they're older," her parents always said.

We ate the food that was placed in front of us.

"What you don't want, no problem. You can eat it later," her parents said with a smile.

If they had chicken, Marine's father got the big piece first. Her mother made sure of that.

We children wondered about it, but we never voiced an opinion. It didn't matter, we were happy with whatever they did. Hmmmm, Granny didn't disappoint us with the delicious feast she placed before us at her table either. The food made you want to lick your fingers. It was awesome and so good.

"I can see you all are enjoying yourselves very much," Granny smiled at us. "Eat all you want, my precious ones. I love people to appreciate my cooking."

After dinner, Marine and her sisters were so full.

"We want to run and play. We love to exercise. Can we go out and explore the farm?" they asked.

The adults agreed. "There's a lot to see and do but be careful. Don't get into any trouble. Remember what Dad and Mom talk to you guys about the dos and don'ts on the farm. Go enjoy yourselves."

Marine and her sisters laughed as they walked outside through the backdoor into the yard. It was enchanting, there were animals running around, shady trees with all sorts of lounge chairs to relax in.

We wanted to do something stimulating. Who should we chase first? All the colorful chickens that were running around was very tempting.

They decided to hop and dance with the chickens around the yard. Chickens can run and jump. They made a lot of noise when they tried to catch one.

Wow! Chickens can fly. They did and got away from us. They will also fly at you if they feel endangered. We weren't going to hurt them. We love animals. We have a dog and one of our cousins has a cat that we play with on our visit to their house. Granny said she would show us how to get a chicken ready for cooking. What did she mean? We were not sure about it. We will have to wait and see. We only knew about getting chicken from the market.

They ran over to check out the pigpen.

They looked very large to us. Granny said they could be hard to handle if they don't know you.

"Look, but don't touch them. The pigs will oink you."

They all laughed at the sound of the oinking pigs. It was so funny to them.

"Okay. Let us explore over there."

They started walking towards the barn. Marine and her sisters stopped abruptly at the barn door. They did not enter. Granny stated that there were horses in there. Marine was the leader of the group. She always listened to the adults. Marine's parents trusted her with her younger siblings. She was very responsible and loved them.

"Everyone would be devastated if any of us got hurt. The horses do not know you. They are not a toy to be played with. Granny will show us the horses later. Maybe even let us ride one. We have plenty of time. The family will be here for weeks or maybe all summer long," Marine explained to her siblings.

Marine and her sisters turned the corner of the barn. There was a pond nearby. They walked over to it, bent, and looked at their reflections in the water staring back at them. They made funny faces that were so funny to all of them. They splashed the water on each other. As they stood up straight, they looked in the direction of the other side of the pond. Wow! Far in the distance was a beautiful tree on a hill. They had not noticed the tree driving past that area before on the way to Granny's house. They were just too excited to see her. The children don't know how they missed it. If you looked in that direction you can't miss it. It is breathtaking. They know grand when they see it. Marine and her sisters were so excited about their find.

"Let's run over there and play!"

They were separated from the pond by a field of beautiful flowers everywhere in all the colors of life. The children laughed as they ran through the field to get to their destination, the spectacular tree. Such a dazzling sight. A pathway led up to the tree. Marine ran up to hug it. She loves nature.

"Hello!"

Her sister watched Marine greet the tree from a few feet away. The children waited on Marine's signal that it was okay to approach the tree. She stepped away and waved to her sister to step forward. She introduced everyone.

"We are from the city, far, far away from here. We are visiting our Granny who lives over there."

 Marine pointed in the direction of Granny's house. The tree knew it well. Over the years the tree had seen people come and go. The tree loved to watch as Granddad and Grandmother worked on the farm above them on the hill.

"We like it here," the children all said at the same time. "Can we play and have fun here?"

The tree shook signaling a yes. They started to sing and dance around the tree, laughing as they chased each other around.

"You can't catch me!" "Yes, I can!"

The tree was so delighted to hear the children playing so happily again. He could almost forget the past. The tree shook a little, sending leaves everywhere. The children raised their hands as the leaves fell around them.

A new generation has come to play.